BEEKEEPING

A Novice's Guide

2nd Edition

Words and
Photographs
by David Wootton

PUBLISHING

First published in Great Britain in 2010 by:
David Wootton Publishing.

2nd Edition printed 2011

Copyright 2011 David Wootton
Copyright all photography: David Wootton Photography
Additional Photography: Helen Wootton

Photo Credit - Honey bee with varroa mite
Stephen Ausmus: United States Department of Agriculture

Editing and proofreading: Elaine Swift www.elaineswift.co.uk

A CIP Catalogue of this book is available from the British Library.

ISBN: 978-0-9566877-1-5

Designed and typeset by
www.chandlerbookdesign.co.uk

Printed in Great Britain by
Ashford Colour Press Ltd.

Acknowledgements

A big thank you to my mentors, Terry and Lorraine Gibson. First for the numerous phone calls and emails I made to them as I learnt the art of beekeeping and secondly for very kindly helping me with this book. It would not have been possible without their expertise and patience.

Thank you also to my wife, Helen, for her patience as I wrote this book and spent many evenings in the shed building hives and frames. I also apologise for the times I asked her to assist me with a 'quick job', telling her there was no need to kit up, and then she ended up being stung. This happened on more than one occasion.

I also thank all those beekeepers who read the first edition and contacted me with comments and objective criticism.

Finally thank you to Gill Smith at E.H. Thorne, for supplying me with a national hive to enable me to photograph the construction of the hive and frames.

Contents

Introduction

For a few years I had watched a wild colony of honey bees coming and going from a hollow brick gate pillar near my home. I had even seen them swarm without knowing the reason for this. I was fascinated by the bees' activities and this led me to think it would be fun to have my own hives.

Having made the decision, I started researching how to go about it. Numerous books, magazines and the internet gave me all manner of advice on how to get started. However the more I read, the more daunting it all seemed: especially as some of the advice seemed contradictory.

After much research I took the necessary steps to becoming a beekeeper. Four years on I have eight hives, my bees are thriving and have given me some bumper harvests of honey.

Most of the guidance I found informed me that keeping a few colonies of bees was easy and relatively cheap. I don't want to put anyone off but you do have to be committed. I discovered there was a lot more to it than some of the books and articles I'd read lead me to believe.

It's reported that the large number of new beekeepers taking up the pastime will create problems in the future. As the saying goes, "A puppy is not just for Christmas." Well, it also applies to bees and new beekeepers.

Please don't get me wrong as it's great fun and I have thoroughly enjoyed looking after my bees, but all the information you receive can become a bit daunting. The terminology used can also be confusing. So, for this reason, I've written a glossary of terms that I wish I'd had when I started out.

As a professional photographer I've been regularly taking photographs of my bees and beekeeping, and was therefore fortunate to be able illustrate this book with my images. I felt that visually seeing the hive, equipment and steps you need to take, would inspire and help would-be beekeepers to understand what they need to do to fulfil their dream of keeping honey bees on a small scale.

Most of the books on the subject are written by experts who assume you know something about beekeeping. I was lucky to meet a couple, who with years of beekeeping experience, kindly acted as my mentors as I learnt how to keep bees, and they helped me to write this book.

This book is not an expert's view on how to keep bees: there are plenty of those. It is an aid to discovering the pleasure of how to keep bees as a hobby. It's written in layman's language by someone, who only a short while ago, was in the same position you're in now. It covers the advice I got and I have tried to simplify the practical side of beekeeping, which I have only just learnt and am still learning.

Honey bee collecting nectar from a crocus flower

Thankfully I believe I have not made any major mistakes. My bees seem content with their coming and going from the hives, and if success is measured in the quality of honey they've produced, then I think I'm succeeding.

One thing you'll realise is that every beekeeper you meet will have a different opinion on every aspect of beekeeping. I've heard it said, that if you ask a question to 10 beekeepers you'll get 10 different answers. Having published the first edition of this book in October 2010 I can now say this is spot on!

I've received numerous comments from readers who were not novices, some saying what I wrote was wrong and others saying it was correct. Some criticised me for writing the book in the first place as a novice without any beekeeping experience. As I have pointed out to them, they have missed the point of the book. It is written by a novice, for novice's, to demonstrate that taking up beekeeping doesn't need to be complicated.

However, as with all experiences in life, learning, practising and experimenting is part of the pleasure of being the guardian of your own bees.

Getting started

"Don't be afraid to ask"

So you've made the biggest decision you are going to make in beekeeping and that's deciding to become a beekeeper. But what do you do now?

Don't worry: I was in exactly the same position. I had sat for hours at my computer surfing the internet and you will no doubt do the same. But what really got me going was joining my local beekeeping association.

I found my local association - the West Norfolk and King's Lynn Beekeeping Association (WNKLBA) - with a quick search in Google. If you can't find yours by an internet search, go to your National Beekeeping Association website. Most countries have one and they should be able to link you to your local association or club. There is no better place to start.

As I found, your local association will run beginners' courses and during the winter months, theory courses are the perfect way to find out about your new hobby. These courses are designed to give you the basic knowledge about bees, the hive, inspections and how to get started. Come the spring, when the hives can be opened, the course

will allow you to get your first practical experience of handling bees in a hive. Lifting your first frame of active bees from a hive is a great experience.

There are so many advantages to joining your local association. It's not expensive to join and usually comes with third party liability and hive insurance. But the main advantage is that you get the opportunity to meet experienced beekeepers. All the ones I've met have been only too pleased to answer my questions.

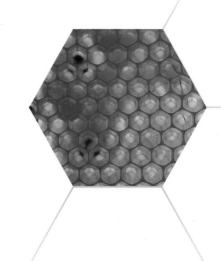

Beekeeper inspecting
frames in a super

My course tutor said, "The only stupid question is the one that's not asked." This is true, so don't be afraid to ask - however stupid you think your question might be. The theory course I took ran over three evenings, in which we were introduced to the honey bee via a PowerPoint presentation.

Throughout their lives bees have a specific role within the hive. This is very important in beekeeping and I will cover it in a subsequent chapter.

The practical courses took place at the association apiary, and when spring arrived, new members split into small groups, each with an experienced beekeeper.

First we were taught how to dress correctly, which helps if you want to avoid unnecessary stings. We were also taught how to light our smoker without it going out just as it was needed. Once we were ready, the roof of the hive was removed and we took our first look at the working innards. We each took turns to remove a couple of frames and our instructors pointed out the working bees, the drones, and if we were lucky: the queen.

You will soon be able to spot the eggs, larvae, capped brood, and the pollen cells plus sealed honey cells when you inspect the frames within the hive.

If you are lucky you will meet an experienced beekeeper who will be willing to act as your mentor. I was fortunate enough to meet a married couple who made it so much easier for me to start up. It's great if you have someone on the end of the telephone or email to answer questions if you're uncertain about something.

Your association will also run other courses and events throughout the year. These courses go into more detail on specialist subjects such as diseases, how to winter your bees, extracting honey, and wax products etc. The more you can learn the easier it will be to keep bees. Once you've completed your course you should have the confidence to make a start.

There's no rush as it will be some time before you can start your first colony. However now is the time to prepare by putting together the equipment you need. You may want to purchase your first hive ready assembled, complete with frames and foundation. I enjoy making my hives from pre-cut kits. I find it therapeutic spending the winter evenings in my shed building the hives rather than watching yet more celebrity reality shows on television. Anyone with an ounce of DIY skill can do it.

Hints & tips

- **Find yourself a mentor**

- **Build your own hives and frames, it's enjoyable and cheaper**

New beekeepers and instructor at a local association apiary opening a National hive

The hive

"Part by part"

You can buy a number of different hives. You may come across names such as the Langstroth, Smith, Dadant, Dartington and Commercial hives. Each country seems to have its own designs and preferences.

Beekeepers are also experimenting with Top Bar hives, which are traditionally used in Africa. However in the United Kingdom hobby and small-scale beekeepers mainly use the National and WBC hives.

With its gable roof and slanting sides, the WBC is perhaps what most people imagine a hive to look like. It is double skinned with the working part encased within an outer wooden wall. Some beekeepers like this, one because of its looks and also because the double skin means the timber used doesn't have to be so thick and heavy.

However, the majority of beekeepers in Britain use the National Beehive. I decided on this version, basically because it's easy to buy all the parts and they can be switched between hives. In general, hive parts are not interchangeable

due to the different dimensions. The one exception is that frames can be swapped between WBC and National hives as their dimensions are identical. Whichever type of hive you decide on, the principles of how they are used are basically the same: it's just the dimensions that are different.

A beehive is a layer of boxes. As bees tend to work upwards within the colony, the first or lowest box (brood box) is where the queen lays her eggs and the colony feeds and raises the bee larvae until they emerge. Above this, different layers of boxes are added to where the bees store their food (honey). Controlling where they store this honey enables us to harvest it.

When you've decided what type of hive you want, you need to choose whether to build your own or to buy a readymade one. You can buy a completed hive already constructed with frames included. Or you can buy pre-cut kits that you can assemble yourself with a bit of time, glue and nails,

I thoroughly enjoy building my own hives and frames, and if you have any DIY skills you won't find it too difficult. When you purchase your first hive, my advice is to buy the best you can afford.

Hives made from red cedar wood are widely acknowledged as the best. Pine and other types of wood are perfectly acceptable, but in general, need much more care and maintenance.

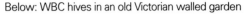

Below: WBC hives in an old Victorian walled garden

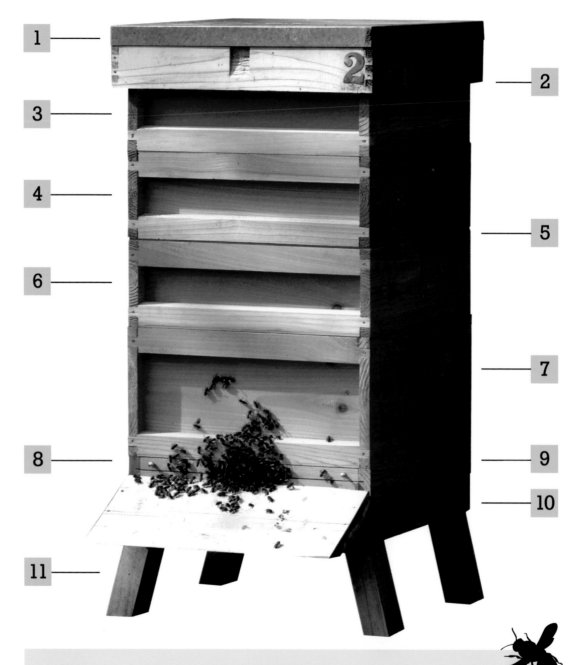

1. Flat roof
2. Crown board under roof
3. 2nd super
4. 1st super
5. Queen excluder
6. Half size brood box
7. Brood box
8. Entrance block
9. Wire mesh floor
10. Hive stand with alighting board
11. Legs

Plastic hives are new on the market and I've heard some say they could have a lack of ventilation, which could create condensation problems within the hive. The one person I know using a plastic hive hasn't had this problem so this view may be incorrectly circulated by traditionalists who believe a hive can only be made of wood.

He has enjoyed using the plastic hive and his only concern is about the position of the frames. Where they are placed means he often has to stop himself from standing in front of the entrance when he's inspecting.

I do foresee a problem with internal cleaning during the spring clean. With a wooden hive, brood boxes, floors etc. are exchanged for cleaned ones before they are cleaned internally with a blowtorch to kill any pests and diseases. Of course this method can't be used on plastic.

I understand that with a plastic hive either the frames have to be removed to another hive or pushed to one end whilst you clean the insides with a water and soda crystal solution.

The big advantage of the plastic hive is that it will last for decades without any maintenance, and some people may like its modern sculptured appearance. The choice will come down to personal preference.

I'm sure there are pros and cons with both wooden and plastic hives.

When I started, I found it confusing trying to understand which part of a hive did what, plus some beekeepers give each part alternative names. I have, therefore, written brief details with photographs to help you recognise the individual parts and their practical uses.

As a novice the most essential parts needed for your first hive, and to get you started, are:

- a wire mesh floor
- an entrance block
- a brood box with deep frames of foundation
- a queen excluder
- two supers with shallow frames
- a crown board
- a roof

Each individual part of a hive sits on top of each other and does not need any fittings to hold it in place. Once bees are in the hive they will seal the joints, and the weight of the parts and honey stores will keep it in place.

Above: Inspecting a plastic hive

Opposite page: Shows all the equipment required to get started

15

The hive in parts

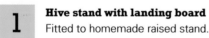

1 **Hive stand with landing board**
Fitted to homemade raised stand.

2 **Wire mesh floor / varroa mite board**
Board can be slid out for inspections.

1. Hive stand and landing board

This is the bottom part of the hive and is often fitted with a sloping landing board for the bees to land on when they return from a foraging flight. You can fit short legs, but I've found building my own stands raises the hive so I don't get backache from bending down to it. Breezeblocks are also useful for raising the hive, but perhaps don't look so attractive in a garden.

2. Wire mesh floor and varroa mite board

The wire mesh floor is placed onto the hive stand next. As they move about in the hive, your bees will drop pieces of dirt, wax and comb, plus varroa mites as they die or are groomed off. This debris will fall through the mesh and collect onto the mite board which slides in below. The board doesn't have to be in place at all times, only when you're monitoring any infestation. Fitting it for short periods (one week) will enable you to see the level of any infestation. The mesh floor also enables ventilation, as a flow of air through the hive is essential.

3 **Entrance block**
Showing narrow entrance when in place.

4 **Empty brood box**
With metal runners which frames sit on.

3. Entrance block

The entrance block is a piece of wood that fits into the front of the hive. Its narrow opening allows bees to come and go. When the colony is small, the narrow entrance is easily protected against any intruders. As the colony grows, the entrance block can be partially pulled out to give a larger entrance and at times can be fully removed. However, as wild bees have a narrow entrance to protect, some experts believe a hive should also have one and advocate leaving the entrance block in place all year round. This is especially important in late summer when robbing wasps are prevalent.

4. Empty brood box

The brood box, also known as the deep box, is where the majority of the colony will live on frames. This is where the queen will lay her eggs and the young bees will feed the larvae. The box is a dark sanctuary for the bees and will be kept at a constant 35c (95f) in temperature. This is where your colony will cluster to see out the winter months.

National hives with gable and flat roofs

6. Queen excluder

Once your bee colony has expanded, the bees will need more room to leave their stores of honey. We beekeepers want the stores of honey to be clear of any eggs and larvae. So before adding a super, add a queen excluder between the brood box and the super.

Queen excluders are made of plastic, galvanized steel, or wire mesh. They all allow the worker bees to pass through, but not the larger queen and drones. The queen will therefore always remain in the brood box laying her eggs.

7. Empty super with metal castellations

You will add a super when your colony needs the extra space to expand into. A super is the same dimension as the brood box, but not as deep. Shallow frames are placed in it and these can be spaced using plastic or metal spacers. My preference is to use metal castellations, which are attached to the side of the super with slots to take the individual frames, and space them at the correct distance.

8. Super with ten frames

My choice is to use ten frames in a super. Supers can contain between eight to eleven frames, but personal preference is always the deciding factor. Depending on the season, you will need to keep an eye on how quickly your bees are filling the super. During a good supply of pollen and nectar it's not unknown for bees to fill a super within a week. Keep adding new ones as your supers fill: it's far better to have too many on than not enough.

5. Brood box frames and dummy board

Wooden frames with wax foundation are placed within the brood box. A brood box generally has 11 to 12 frames in place. I have 11 frames plus a dummy board. It's on these frames that your bees will draw out the wax foundation to create the cells in which the queen will lay her eggs and where the workers will store nectar and pollen. In very strong colonies the brood box can be increased in size by adding a super with frames on top. Adding a super as a half sized brood box will give extra space for the queen to lay her eggs.

The dummy board is used as the first end frame. It's first to be removed when you're doing an inspection and therefore last to be returned to the hive. It fills the space between the first frame and outer wall, preventing burr comb from being built in the space. And when closing up the hive, you can add the board to prevent rolling which will damage your bees.

5 **Brood box with frames**
Dummy board showing as the
end frame.

6 **Queen excluder**
With slots running at right angles to
the frames.

7 **Empty super with metal castellations**
Plastic or metal spacers can also
be used.

8 **Super with ten frames**
Choice of eight to ten frames in
your hive.

9. Deep and shallow frames

The frames are where your bees will build their comb. Deep frames are used within the brood box and shallow frames in supers. When new, frames have wax foundation in them which the bees will draw out. Each sheet of wax foundation is wired to help rigidity and to hold them together when placed in a honey extractor. If you like comb honey it is possible to get unwired shallow foundations, which will enable you to cut out blocks of honey to enjoy.

10. Crown board

In simple terms this is the ceiling of the hive and is the last thing to go on top of the boxes before you put the roof on. One or two holes are cut into the board: these are either feeding holes or are used to place a bee escape when you clear bees out of the supers to extract the honey. Other than when you're feeding or clearing, the crown board holes remain covered. A piece of heavy card will do, however I had a local glazier hone the edges of some thick glass which I use to cover the holes.

11. Roof

As stated this is the top of the hive. Most National hives have a flat roof though gable roofs are available if you wish to make your hive more attractive. Each roof is designed to keep water out and has ventilation ducts to enable the free flow of air through the hive.

12. Eke

An Eke is a shallow frame of wood, the same dimensions as the brood box and supers. It can be placed on top of the boxes to create a space between the tops of the frames and crown board for administering certain kinds of varroa treatment or winter feed in the form of fondant. When administering treatment or fondant you will find the crown board and roof will not fit without an Eke in place. If you do not have one an empty super can be used to serve the same function.

A National Hive on a homemade raised stand

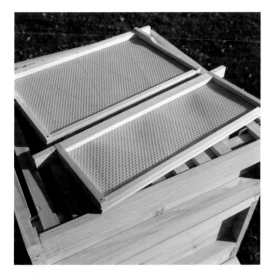

9 **Deep and shallow frames**
Wire supports can be seen in wax foundation.

10 **Crown board**
Showing holes for feeding or bee escapes.

11 **Flat roof**
Gable roofs are also available.

12 **Eke**
An empty super can also be used as a spacer.

Constructing a National Hive

"It's not difficult"

Like me, many of you will enjoy making your own hives and frames from pre-cut kits. A number of manufacturers offer hives as a flat pack option and these are less expensive as you don't pay the manufacturer's build costs. Delivery costs too are cheaper than a constructed hive with all its bulk.
Making a beehive and its frames is not hard and there are a few tips that will probably help you avoid expensive mistakes. Making your own hives will give you a greater understanding of the hive. It's also a task you can do during the winter months in preparation for a new season or whilst you are eagerly awaiting your first bees.

I have used the National Hive type to describe the construction of the frames and the hive itself, and continue to use it as a reference throughout this book.

Making the brood box and supers for a National hive

The brood box and super are similar in construction. The main difference is that one is deeper than the other.

Equipment you will need to make the hive:

1. Good size hammer
2. Small hammer
3. Long-nosed pliers
4. Set-square
5. Pencil
6. Wood glue
7. Block of wood
8. 2 inch and 1 ½ inch nails (5.1cm and 3.8cm). (These usually come with hive kits)
9. ½ inch pins (1.27cm) (These usually come with hive kits)

Hive parts needed to construct one brood box or a super:

1. 2x outer walls (with tongue and groves cut out)
2. 2x inner walls
3. 2x square top bars
4. 2x sloping bottom bars
5. 2x metal frame runners (brood box only)
6. 2x plastic frame runners or metal castellations (supers only)

Hints & tips

- Place parts in rough positions to give yourself a mental picture of how the box is going to fit together before you start the actual construction.

Starting with the construction of the brood box, lay out all the parts you need and familiarise yourself with each one.

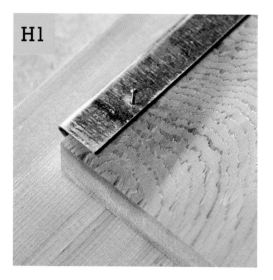

H1

Once you're happy to make a start, first attach a frame runner to each of the inner walls using ½ inch pins (see image H1). The pins can be fiddly to hold and hammer into place, so I find long nosed pliers help to grip the pins so you can hammer them in (see image H9).

When you've done both runners, place the inner walls to one side. Next take an outer wall and draw a 7/16 inch (1.1 cm) line from the

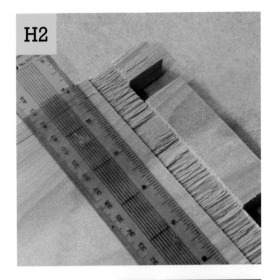

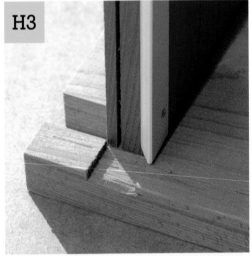

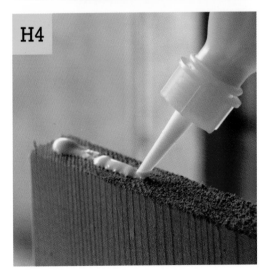

top edge (see image H2). Repeat this on the second outer wall.

With one of the outer walls flat on your workbench, practise fitting an inner wall with runner attached into the chiselled grove and copy at the other end. Glue along the edge and fit into position if they fit neatly and snugly together. Make sure the top edge of the runner is level with the line you drew along the top of the outer wall (see image H3).

You should now have an outer wall flat on your bench with two inner walls rising vertically. Check that both runners are on the inside of the box.

Apply glue along both edges of the vertical inner walls (see image H4). Line up and fit the remaining outer wall to form a cube. Again, make sure the runner is lined up to the marked line. You should be able to push the parts together and then hammer into place for a tight fit. Use a block of wood between the hammer and hive parts so you don't damage the wood (see image H5).

When you have constructed the four walls, use a set square to check the box is square, gently shifting the sides to get them straight. Remember it's not nailed together yet, so don't force anything (see image H6).

Now to give the box some rigidity you need to fix the top and bottom bars in place. These bars look similar and it's easy to mix them up. Take hold of all four bars, hold them together and view the ends. You will see that two are square and two are sloping. Divide the four bars into two groups: each with one square and one sloping end. To fit the bars, gently

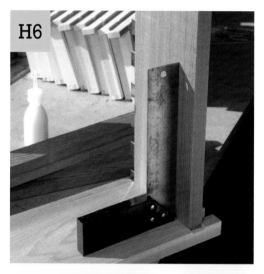

turn the box, so that it sits on your bench with the outer wall tongue and grooves uppermost. Place glue into the groves and along the edges where the top and bottom bars will sit.

Next place the top and bottom bars and push into the groves (see image H7). Make sure the square top bar is at the top where the runners are, and the sloping bar is at the bottom. I know

from experience it's very easy to get these the wrong way round. Now they are in place, you will need to hammer down the top and bottom bars to fit tight. When you have completed one side, roll the box to the other side and repeat. Again use a block of wood between the hammer and the hive to protect the wood (see image H8).

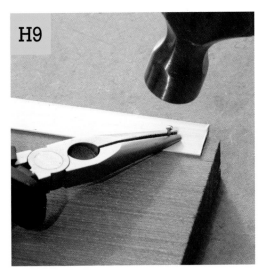

H9

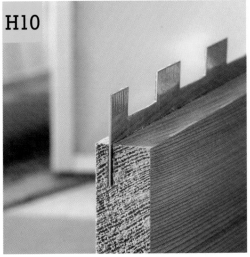

H10

I have described above how to construct a brood box. The principles are the same when building a super, except in your choice of plastic runners or metal castellations. Plastic runners are fitted in the same way as metal runners, except the plastic ones which are supplied don't usually have pre-drilled holes (see hive H9). If you choose to fit metal castellations in your supers, some National

Hive kits will have a saw cut into which your castellation fits (see image H10).

If there isn't a saw cut, the castellation will need to be pinned (as with runners) centrally along the top of the inner wall. Make certain that the castellation cut outs are ¼ inch (6.35mm) above the inner wall edge.

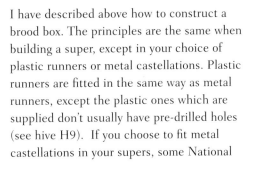

Hints & tips

- Red cedar is a very durable timber. However, it is soft so don't hammer the wood directly: place a block of wood between the hammer and hive to protect it.

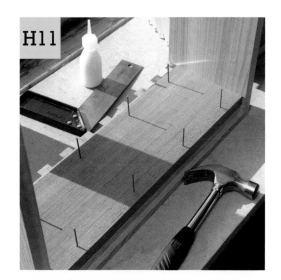

Hints & tips

• Tip: As you construct your hive keep checking it's square, especially before nailing together.

Nailing the hive

Before you nail the hive, it's important that the brood box or super is square, so check and ease the walls over to get it square. Before nailing, I go around each side of the box with a block of wood and hammer, knocking together each joint. You can hammer quite hard as this tightens every joint before you finally hammer in the nails.

The first nails go in the inside the box. Use 1 ½ inch (3.8 cm) nails to hold in place the top and bottom bars to the inner wall (see image H11). Check the line-up of the nails before hammering them in, as it's easy to miss the top and bottom bars.

Next, nail the four corners of the box using 2-inch (5.1 cm) nails. These nails are hammered into the tongue on the top and bottom bars (see image H12). Finally hammer in 2-inch (5.1cm) nails through the outer walls and into the inner walls at all four corners (see image H13). You may want to use four nails at this point on the brood box, but three will be ample when you nail the supers.

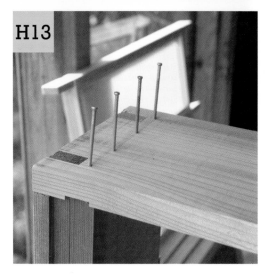

27

Making up Frames of Foundation

"It gets easier the more you make up"

Two types of frames are used within the hive. Deep frames are used in the brood box where the majority of the bees live and the queen lays her eggs. Shallow frames are used in the supers where your bees will store their honey.

As a novice, looking through an equipment supplier's brochure or website, I assume like me you will find the number of different frame types and parts very confusing. Each is coded depending on a variety of measurements. However when you're starting out, most equipment retailers will supply you with self-spacing standard deep frames for your brood box, and standard shallow frames. These will fit either into metal castellations in your supers or will need plastic or metal spacers that slide onto the ends of the top bar (see image F1).

However, the construction principle is the same whichever type of frame you are making. In the example images I have used a Hoffman self-spacing DN4 frame. This is a standard self-spacing frame used in the brood box many novices will start with. When you start to make your frames, I suggest you begin with the larger brood ones, and when you've completed

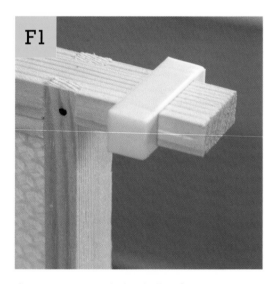

F1

them, continue with the shallow frames. You will spot differences but none that makes their construction any different.

Hints & tips

- Your first frame will take you some time, but I can assure you, your hundredth frame will be made in no time at all.

Equipment you will need to make frames:

1. Small hammer
2. Modelling knife
3. ¾ inch (1.9 cm) frame nails. (These usually come with frame kits).

Parts needed to construct one frame:

1. 1x top bar
2. 2x side bars
3. 2x bottom bars
4. 1x wedge bar
5. 1x sheet of wired wax foundation

If you have a work-bench, make sure it's clear as this will enable you to have a small production line to make your frames.

Firstly lay out in front of you all the parts of one standard brood frame. The top bar will have the wedge bar still attached to it. Using the modelling knife run the blade along each side of the wedge bar to cut it free, then trim off any wood splinters (see image F2).

Next, fit the top bar into the cut grove in one of the side bars. Repeat on the other side. A gentle tap with the hammer will fit them tightly together. Make sure the side bars are facing the correct way, with the groves facing inwards to allow the wax sheet to slide into position (see image F3).

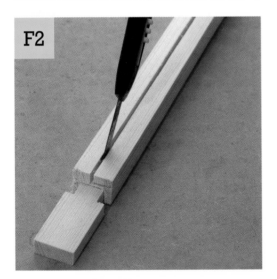

F2

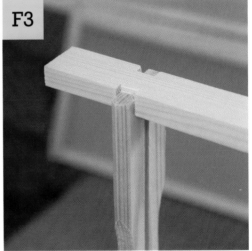

F3

Hints & tips

- Wired wax foundation is used in frames to give added strength when spun in a honey extractor. Unwired foundation is used when you want to take comb honey from a frame.

With both side bars connected to the top bar, turn the frame over and fit one of the bottom bars into the slot at the bottom of the side bars (see image F4). When it's in place, I prefer not to have the bottom bar fitting flush in each of the side bar slots. I find it's easier to slide in the sheets of foundation if the side bars are leaning slightly outwards.

Next, take a sheet of wired brood wax foundation. When you hold it against the light, you will see the wire looping through the wax. On the longest sides of the sheet, you'll see the wire protrudes before looping back into the wax.

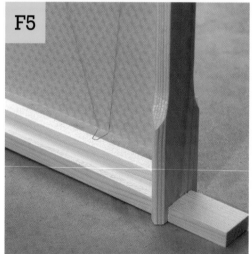

Take the side on which the three wire loops are the longest and bend each wire 90 degrees to the wax. Having done this, slide the sheet of wax into the frame along the groves on each of the side bars. The sheet of wax should fall into place with the folded wired edge now resting on the underside of the top bar (see image F5).

Fit the second bottom bar into the empty side bar slot making certain that the wax sheet is free and fits between both bottom bars. Make sure also that the wax sheet sits in the groves running along each side of the side bars.

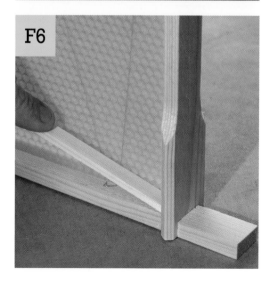

When everything is in place, fit the wedge bar to the underside of the top bar covering the three bent wires, and wedge in the sheet of wax foundation (see image F6).

With the frame parts all in place, I use a light hammer to gently tap each end to fit tightly and to get the side, top and bottom bars perpendicular to each other. Glue is not needed when making up your frames. Once you are happy that the frame is square, you can nail it together.

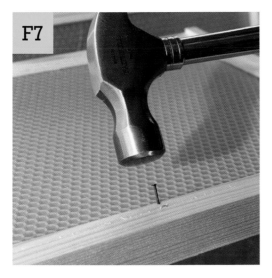

F7

F8

F9

Nailing the frame

With experience you will find your preferred order of nailing the frame parts. My preferred order is wedge bar, top/side bars, and finally bottom bars.

Wedge bar: three nails. Hammer in the nails at an angle to hold the wedge bar in position. Make sure the nail goes through the folded wire in the sheet of wax foundation locking the sheet of wax in position. Always angle the nail to hold the wire and to prevent it protruding through to the other side of the wood. A protruding nail will catch your hive tool when you are scraping a frame, or you will catch a finger on it which is painful!(see image F7).

Top bar/side bars: four nails. Hammer in a nail on both sides of each of the side bars nailing them to the top bar (see images F8 and F9).

Hints & tips

- If sheets of foundation are too pliable due to warm temperatures, a few minutes laid flat in a deep freeze will make them stiffen and it will be easier to fit them into the frames.

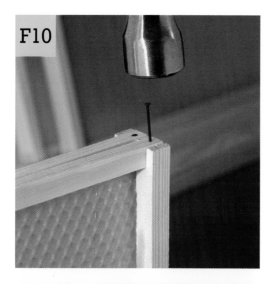

F10

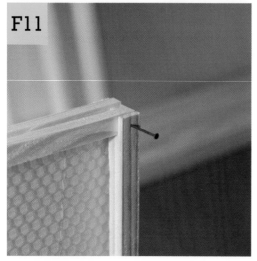

F11

Bottom bars: four nails. Hammer a nail into each end of the bottom bars to connect them to the side bars. Doing it this way will allow you to remove the bottom bars to replace the wax foundation sheet if you ever need to. As frames are relatively inexpensive I recommend replacing the whole frame and foundation, and so I put a nail through the bottom of both side bars, locking the bottom bars in position (see images F10 and F11).

The frame will be strong and rigid when nailed, and it won't collapse when you lift it out to do a hive inspection. When your bees draw out the wax foundation, they will build their comb within each frame, encasing the wire. You'll be surprised at the weight of a frame when it has brood and capped honey stored in it, so the foundation wire remaining in place gives it strength.

When you've made your deep frames, move onto the shallow frames. As you will see, the construction principle is the same, except that the side bars are flat and not self spacing. However, nail them the same way.

If you want some comb honey, you'll need to use unwired wax foundation in your shallow frames. Frames are made the same way except because it's wireless, when it's nailed your wedge bar will only wedge the sheet of foundation in place. However, as these frames will not be spun, they do not need to be as strong.

Hints & tips

- The wax foundation needs to be flat within a frame because the bees will not draw it out evenly if it's buckled.

F12

Hints & tips

- I mark the top bar/spacers of unwired frames 'NW' so I can easily see they should not be put in an extractor. Other people place a drawing pin as a mark at one end of the top bar. Mark frames as you wish, however you do need to be able to spot them, as it's nearly impossible to see the foundation wire within a frame when it's full of capped honey (see image F12).

Making up a frame of wax foundation

Equipment

"Buy it as you need it"

You'll need a number of items of equipment from the start. This equipment will enable you to make the necessary hive inspections in your first year. They can all be bought from bee equipment suppliers either from their outlets or online. As time progresses there will be other equipment you may wish to purchase, e.g. a honey extractor, but there is no need to rush into this outlay as your local association should have at least one extractor which will be available for you to hire for a small fee. I have listed below the items you will definitely need to start.

1. Bee suit

There are numerous suits on the market. I suggest you try some on to see which you like best before buying. Some have a fitted round hat and veil whilst others have a fencing style veil. You also have a choice of a full suit or smock. Make sure the elasticated cuffs fit snugly and that the suit has some useful pockets. I originally bought a smock, but now have a full suit, having learnt that when you bend down the smock rides up and a bee can be trapped when you pull it down again. I learnt the hard way when I trapped two bees and got stung twice.

You'll find that children will be fascinated by your bees, so it's worthwhile getting a child's suit and gloves so they can take a closer look at your hives. These are available in various sizes to fit all ages.

Suits are made to fit all including children

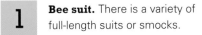

1 **Bee suit.** There is a variety of full-length suits or smocks.

2 **Smoker.** There are various sizes in stainless steel or copper.

3 **Hive tool**. You will need this to hand all the time.

2. Smoker

This is one of your most important tools and there is a great choice to look at. They all do the same thing i.e let you to blow cool smoke when you are inspecting your hives. The cheaper ones are made from galvanized steel and the most expensive are made of copper. They also come in different sizes. The size you choose will depend on the number of hives you have to inspect. As a beginner, you will not have a large apiary so buy an average size smoker and the best you can afford.

3. Hive tool

This two-ended tool is something you cannot work without when inspecting a hive.

The sharper end has two uses. 1) To crack the propolis seal the bees have made when you lift off either the crown board and supers.

2) For scraping away any build-up of wax and propolis from areas where you don't want it. The hook end helps you to lift the frames from the hive. You will find you have the hive tool in your hand at all times.

4. Fuel for your smoker

You need a dry material that will smoulder rather than catch fire. It is possible to buy rolled cardboard smoke cartridges, however I find they burn too quickly and have burnt out before you are finished. I find old hessian sacking the best as it smoulders slowly allowing you to complete your hive inspection in plenty of time. Dry pieces of wood, twigs and bark are also excellent, as is shredded cardboard packaging. I usually put a little of this in with a scrunched up piece of hessian. Make sure any shredded cardboard is clean of any glue or stickers as these can be harmful to the bees and any residue can taint the honey.

5. Gloves

As a first year beekeeper you will probably be keen to wear gloves. Equipment suppliers have a range of light leather gauntlets to choose from. These will enable you to handle your frames while protecting your hands from stings. Some beekeepers like more 'feel' and either do their inspections with bare hands or wear disposable surgical gloves. As your confidence grows you may also wish to use bare hands. I recommend you wear leather gauntlets to start with: especially if you're nervous about being stung,

6. Bee brush

This is a long handled soft haired brush that helps you to move the bees from the edges of your brood box, crown board and roof when closing up your hive. It can also be used by a partner to remove any bees that are clinging to your bee suit when you've finished your inspection.

4 **Fuel for smoker.** Hessian and or cardboard packaging.

5 **Gloves.** Leather and canvas gauntlets.

Feeders

You can buy a number of different types of feeder. Perhaps as you gain more experience you'll want to try more types, but to start with the rapid or contact feeder will let you successfully feed your bees when they need it. Depending on your choice and size of feeder, you will need to place one or two empty supers on the crown board so the hive roof fits when a feeder is in place.

Hints & tips

- 2-litre plastic lemonade bottles are ideal to refill your feeders.

7. Rapid feeder

I prefer this method of feeding. The feeder fits over the crown board hole and you can see the bees climbing up the central aperture to collect the sugar solution, and watch them taking it down into the hive. To refill you only need to remove the hive roof, lift the feeder lid and you can see how much solution is left in the container. The feeder holds just over 2 litres (3.5 pints) of solution, which is generally enough for a couple of days supply. I also find this is the cleanest method, as by carefully refilling, you avoid leaving excess solution which makes a sticky mess on the crown board.

6 **Bee brush.** A soft haired brush to remove bees.

7 **Rapid feeder.** In place on hive with lid open.

8. Contact feeder

This feeder is basically a bucket with a lid and a small mesh-covered opening. Fill the bucket with the sugar solution, fix the lid and invert. Although some solution will drip out, a vacuum will be created which will hold in the remaining solution. I recommend that, when you first invert it, you do it well away from the hive. This prevents dripped sugar solution attracting robbing bees near your hive.

The feeder is then placed over the hole in the crown board and the bees can collect the sugar solution through the mesh opening. The advantage of a contact feeder is that they come in three sizes: 1.0/2.5/4.5 litres (1/4, 1/2, and 1 gallon) capacity. This is useful if you can't visit your hive daily to refill when you are feeding your bees.

8 **Contact feeder**. Showing mesh hole before inverting.

Hive tool in hand removing a wired queen excluder

Using your smoker

Your smoker is an essential piece of equipment and understanding its purpose will help you to use it. Like all wild creatures, bees instinctively know what is happening to them. It is understood that colonies in forests, where wild fires can occur, are sensitive to smoke, which sets off the bees' instinctive alarm bell. With the first smell of smoke, bees will start taking in uncapped nectar and honey, known as engorgement.

The bees collect their stores in the expectation they may need to move home and fast. If the smoke becomes thicker, most of the bees will engorge themselves before taking flight. If it diminishes, and the danger is over, the bees will return the nectar and honey back into the cells.

As beekeepers we smoke our bees to occupy them whilst we carry out our inspections. Some people advocate smoking the entrance and then waiting a few minutes before opening the hive. Once they are engorged with honey, bees are less likely to sting which is why we use smoke. I don't smoke

the entrance of my hives, as I've found it aggravates my bees unnecessarily. As a beginner, you can only judge this by observing how your bees react as you get to know their temperament.

Get used to handling your smoker. Practise well away from your hive before using it for the first time. Light it a few times and see how long your chosen fuel smoulders. Once you're confident you'll find it so much easier to handle when you start using it around a hive: especially if you don't have to keep relighting it.

Hints & tips

- Beware - should you ever need to relight your smoker, never do it with your veil covering your face. Many a beekeeper has painfully experienced hot mesh sticking to their face because their veil has melted when they have blown on the fuel through it.

Light a small piece of your chosen fuel and place it in the smoker. Add more fuel and tightly pack it in. Most beginners don't pack enough in and find their fuel burns too quickly due to the amount of air in the smoker.

Your smoker needs to blow cool white smoke. If you find it's blowing sparks to begin with, wait a bit or add some long fresh grass on top of the fuel. You don't want to singe your bees. Once your hive is open, never blow smoke down into it. Firstly your bees won't like it. Secondly if you do this into the supers where the honey is stored, you will blow in minute carbon deposits, which will show up and taint your honey.

You only need a couple of puffs of smoke to remove bees off the tops of the frames. I've found I seldom do any smoking over the hive when I start my inspection. I give the bees a short puff or two when I close the hive. This encourages them off the edges so I can refit supers, queen excluder, and crown board without crushing the bees. Other than this I seldom need to use the smoker. However, I always have it lit and at hand in case my bees have become a little more agitated for whatever reason.

Once you have completed your inspection, twist and stuff some fresh long grass into the nozzle end. The lack of oxygen will soon extinguish your smoker but be aware that it will still be hot.

It has been known for beekeepers to place their smoker in their shed or the boot of their car only to find they are going up in flames. Also be careful where you tip the burnt cinders: a dry hedge or grassy ditch could easily catch light. If you set the ground alight near to your hives, your bees may leave as they would in the wild.

Above: First inspection of a hive two weeks after having hived a nucleus of bees

Opposite: Bees on the tops of the frames. The view you get when opening a hive.

Hints & tips

- Make sure your smoker is fully out and cool before putting it away.

Bees

"It's a hard life being a honey bee"

There are four main species of honey bee around the world, however, the Western honey bee (Apis Mellifera) is the species that beekeepers generally keep in hives. This species is highly productive in the pollination of plants and produces high quality honey for us to enjoy.

There are three types of bee within a hive: workers, drones and a queen. Each has its own specific position within the colony. It is a misconception that the queen is the ruler of the colony: she is just one part of it. The workers are not there to serve her but to work together for the good of the colony. The queen's only task within the colony is to lay eggs, so that the workers can raise young and so increase the number of bees. In a healthy colony, at the height of summer, numbers within a hive can reach between 50,000 to 60,000. All are workers, except for the one queen and up to 1500 drones.

Workers

Workers make up the majority of the colony and they are all infertile females. The immature young bee is set to work immediately it emerges from its cell.

'Cleaner' is the first role in her lifecycle, preparing the empty cells ready for the queen to lay her eggs. Within a few days she can feed the larvae with pollen and nectar brought in by the older foraging bees. As her glands mature she is next able to cap the larvae and honey cells, plus build new comb within the hive.

Two weeks into her life she will transfer pollen and nectar from the foraging bees and can store this food in the cells. After 18 days, she is nearly mature and with her sting formed she will become an entrance guard.

Once her mandibles and poison glands are matured, she will patrol the entrance to check returning foragers and to evict any intruders. Sniffing each bee, she will know if a bee from another colony is attempting to intrude her hive, and if need be, will kill the intruder with her sting. However, in doing so, she will die too.

She will also at this time take her first short flights just outside the hive entrance. Three weeks into her life, and fully mature, she becomes a forager. For the next three weeks she will collect nectar, pollen, propolis and water bringing it into the hive to pass onto her younger sisters to store.

Honey bee collecting pollen from a quince flower

During her three weeks as a forager she will fly many miles carrying heavy loads of nectar and pollen. She will also have to survive hazards outside the hive such as other insects and birds. If she is successful, she will live a total of six weeks and after all her hard work she will die of exhaustion.

If she is born in late autumn, she will live longer as most of her life will be spent clustered together with the other bees throughout the winter. Come the first signs of spring, she will be out foraging until exhausted.

Drones

There are up to 1500 drones in a colony during the summer months. Drones are male, larger in size and stingless. Their sole purpose within the colony is to mate with a virgin queen.

Within the hive all they do is eat and when looking for a queen to mate with they will fly and mate on the wing.

Drone assembly areas normally occur at heights of 10-40 metres above the ground. Mating will end a drone's life as his sexual organs are ripped from his body as he detaches from the queen, and he dies as he falls. Naturally not all drones find a queen to mate with and as winter approaches the worker bees don't want an unproductive bee eating their food stocks. So the drones are forced from the colony and die from cold or starvation.

The queen

The queen is very important to beekeepers because she lays the eggs that increase the size of the colony. The more worker bees within a hive, the greater the amount of honey stored for us to harvest.

The queen is larger than all the other bees and can be spotted by her elongated body and short wings. She likes to stay hidden in the darkness of a hive, so to help spot her most beekeepers mark her thorax with a coloured mark.

You will soon be able to spot queen cells within your hive. These individual cells look like acorns and hang from the bottom or centre of a frame, and generally appear during April, May and June.

Royal jelly secreted by the workers is fed to the larvae in a queen cell, and once she emerges she will fly within three days to mate. Mating in flight with seven to seventeen drones, she will have received enough sperm to last her egg laying life.

Local association apiary visit to my hives in July. Note 4 supers in place on one of the hives

When she has mated she returns to the colony and starts her egg-laying cycle. To lay an egg the queen backs into a freshly cleaned cell and attaches the tiny rice shaped egg to the back wall. At the height of her productivity she can lay up to 2000 eggs per day.

Queens can live for five to seven years, but by her third year, her fertility may start to decline. The worker bees sense when she comes to the end of her productivity and will raise a new queen. On hatching, the new virgin queen will take over from her mother.

We need the queen to be as productive as possible and so have to kill her at the end of her productivity. We do this either by first allowing the workers to produce a new queen or by introducing a new queen to the colony.

From egg to bee

Most of the brood within the hive will be workers, central in a frame and laid in a number of frames working from the centre to the outside. It takes three days from it being laid for the egg

to hatch into a larva. The young workers feed the larva royal jelly for another three days before feeding it a mixture of pollen and honey. As it grows it sheds its skin and curls up into a 'C' shape in the bottom of the cell. After six days it stops eating. Now straight, and filling the cell, it is ready to be entombed.

The workers cap the cell using a mixture of wax and propolis sealing the larva in. Over the next 12 days the larva pupates changing from a grub to an insect. On completion of this metamorphosis the young honey bee emerges from its cell.

Capped drone cells are usually in clusters in the bottom corner of frames or along the top part of a frame between the two brood boxes, if more than one is used. These areas of drone cells are easy to spot as the cells are larger and dome shaped.

A drone will emerge 24 days after the queen has laid the egg. Queens develop more quickly in their larger acorn sized cells, taking just 16 days overall. We need to keep a special eye on these cells to prevent the colony swarming.

From egg to emerging bee

Workers - 21 days	Drones - 24 days	Queen - 16 days

Capped brood and cells with larvae waiting to be capped

Capped drone cells - pronounced dome shape compared to worker bee capped cells

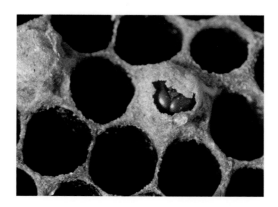

A young bee emerging from its capped cell

Queen cells along the bottom of a frame

Above left: A drone bee on a frame of brood

Above: A marked queen

Opposite: Bees on a frame of capped brood

Propolis

Bees love their propolis and it is very important to them as an anti-bacterial and anti-fungal material. However, it gets everywhere!

Propolis is a sticky resinous substance that bees collect from the bark and buds of trees. It is generally orange-brown in colour and the bees use it to seal gaps in the hive to stop draughts. As you will discover when you open your hive, bees like to seal these gaps and the frames. Use your hive tool to crack these seals so you can remove the frames and hive parts.

Bees also use propolis in the cell walls as an antiseptic to prevent mould and infections. They will also mummify larger creatures which have died in the hive, but are too large to eject. Mummifying the carcass stops it decaying and makes it odourless and harmless to them.

But propolis isn't just used by bees. It's used in alternative medicines and is believed to relieve various conditions including inflammation, viral diseases, ulcers and minor burns. It is also used as a varnish for delicate wood objects such as violins.

Royal jelly

Honey bees secrete royal jelly from their hypopharyngeal glands and feed it to young larvae. They only feed it to them for a few days before feeding them on pollen and nectar. If the colony wishes to produce a new queen, the queen larva is fed only royal jelly. This develops her morphology to induce the development of ovaries which are needed for laying eggs. Royal jelly is much sort after in medicine for its antibiotic characteristics and is also used in some cosmetics.

Opposite: Honey bee
collecting pollen from
blossom on a sloe bush

Bee stings

You will be stung occasionally: it's an occupational hazard! Covering up when you do inspections will help prevent stings, but I find you get stung when you are least expecting it. It can happen if you get little careless and nip a bee - especially if you haven't noticed one still clinging to you when you're removing your bee suit.

It can happen too when you're doing a small job around the hive and haven't covered up. I got stung in my hair for a period after I'd removed the veil. I put this down to the shampoo I'd been using. My wife had bought shampoo containing natural ingredients. I believe some of these may have been bee products, which attracted bees to my head. I've changed shampoo and the problem has gone away.

Your bees will normally be placid, however at times they may seem a little more aggressive. Two possible reasons for this are lack of space or periods when pollen and nectar flow are limited.

When a bee stings it excretes a pheromone. This chemical message signals a danger to other bees causing them to sting as well. Smoking the area where you have been stung will usually work, however if you are uncomfortable, cover the hive and walk away for a few minutes.

Bee stings affect people in different ways: some receive a mild irritation and others can have a serious allergic reaction. When a bee stings it leaves the stinger in the skin which continues to pump venom for up to 20 minutes, so try to remove it as quickly as possible. The sting may be painful for a few hours with swelling and itching for up to a week. An ice pack, or antihistamine tablet or cream may help, as will Piriton™ tablets.

You will need urgent medical attention if you have a serious allergic reaction. Symptoms of an allergic reaction can be a raised rash, headache, fever, severe swelling of the face, tongue and lips, possibly breathing difficulties, and collapse. Anaphylactic shock is deadly serious so do not delay in calling the emergency services. Never be tempted to take someone suffering a severe reaction to hospital yourself. Always call an ambulance and inform the operator that the problem relates to a bee sting.

Hints & tips

• Always put your veil on, no matter how small the job you're doing around your hive.

Above: A varroa mite on the
back of a honey bee

Opposite: Varroa mite visible
on removed drone larvae

Varroa mite

Worldwide media coverage of bee colony deaths
from varroa mite may have started your interest in
bees and beekeeping.

The varroa mite was first discovered in south-east
Asia in the early 1900s and is now found globally,
except in Australia. This mite is a virulent parasite
that lives on brood and bees, feeding off their
bodily fluids. It carries viruses and can cause
deformity in young bees. In extreme cases the
mite will kill whole colonies.

Varroa mites are reddish brown in colour and approximately 1.2mm in size. They are difficult to spot but can sometimes be seen clinging to the bodies of adult bees, though usually only when infection levels are high. A simpler way to spot infestation in a hive is in the larvae, and most notably in drone larvae.

Drone larvae are the mites' preferred breeding site. For this reason many beekeepers remove excess drone brood and inspect it to see if the mite is present. Some beekeepers suggest having one shallow frame within the brood box onto which the bees will create only drone brood which will hang from the bottom bars.

If ample drone brood is visible on other frames, this drone brood comb can be removed from the hive and inspected. It's essential to remove the drone comb beneath the frame once it has been capped otherwise you will have created a varroa nursery.

I have tried this and it works well. It's easy to spot the reddish brown mite against the white larvae when the cells are opened up. There are a number of chemical treatments we can use to control mites. Also, hives have wire mesh floors to make it easier to see dead or groomed mites that have fallen through onto the board.

If you carry out your annual mite treatment in the autumn, seeing the occasional varroa mite, alive or dead, is not a problem. However, the mites are contagious and can easily be spread by drones or swarms. So, if you see greater numbers, you must speak to an expert beekeeper or report it to your local government bee inspector.

Much research is being carried out worldwide on the varroa mite, and although it may not lead to its elimination, it may be controlled in the future.

Bumblebees

Once I became a beekeeper my eyes were opened to the many different types of bee that I hadn't really noticed before. I thought there were honey bees and one species of bumblebee in my area: the big fat yellow and black one. I have since discovered there are about 250 species of bumblebees worldwide, 65 species in Europe, and about 30 types of bumblebee and solitary bees in the UK.

Bumblebee nests are much smaller than those of the honey bee and are found in small cavities under sheds, cracks in the ground, dry hedgerows, and sometimes in old bird boxes.

The queen bumblebee searches out her nest which will already have bedding material in place to keep it warm and insulated. Having mated she hibernates over winter and at the first sign of spring starts to lay her eggs.

Bumblebee colonies are not large, and though they collect pollen and nectar, it's only for their own use and to feed the young.

At the end of summer the queen will lay eggs to produce new queens. Once the new queens emerge, they will mate and search for their own nest. The worker bees, drones and the old queen will perish as the temperature drops and the first frosts of winter arrive.

We have all seen bumblebees slowly flying about in our homes, especially in late summer, even though there are no flowers for them to seek out. These are new queens looking for a hole to investigate, hoping to find an ideal location for her nest. By opening a window you will enable her to look elsewhere. Gardeners are the biggest killer of bumblebees, especially those who use pesticides. So think before you treat those weeds as you may well inadvertently spray a bumblebee nest.

Bumblebee with its proboscis extended into a flower

Where to place your hive

"Don't upset the neighbours"

Before you buy a hive, think carefully about where you are going to place it as you can't move it within a three-mile radius once your bees are in place. You could cause the death of a sizeable proportion of the colony if you do have to move it.

Bees very soon know the exact location of their hive. However, although they are undoubtedly clever creatures, move a hive 10 metres, or even turn it 180 degrees, and the bees will not find the entrance and will therefore die.

If you do ever have to move a hive, you'll need to relocate it more than three miles away for a minimum of two weeks. Once the bees have established their new location, they can be relocated to your newly chosen spot.

Bees will generally live anywhere, but you will help them by thinking about where you place your hive, whether you're in a rural or urban location. Of course, closeness to pollen and nectar sources will help, but bees are known to travel up to five miles in search of it.

When choosing your location, you also have to think about who else your bees might affect. For example being too close to a neighbour's garden, which they and their children regularly use, is not the ideal place.

Placing your hive in a small garden is all right. It will help if you have a fence or high bush a few paces in front of the hive, as this will make the bees rise and descend quickly when they leave and return to the hive.

Hints & tips

• Choose your hive location carefully and try to stick with it.

Opposite: Beekeepers inspecting a Dartington Hive in a wood

I was advised to place my bees where they caught the early morning sun. Catching the eastern sunrise warms the hive and the bees will therefore leave early in the day to start foraging.

Although bees like the sun and its warmth, don't have the hive too exposed to direct sunshine during the hottest part of the day. Dappled shade at midday is perhaps the best solution. Also think about what is above your hive, especially if it is placed on the edge of trees. On windy days a constant tapping from a branch will agitate your bees, and should a bow break and fall, it could cause major damage to the hive and colony.

Many urban beekeepers keep their hives on the roofs of buildings or on waste ground alongside rail tracks. The famous London department stores of Harrods and Fortnum and Mason have hives on their roofs. I've also heard of a city beekeeper who lives in a tower block and has two hives on his balcony. His neighbours think they are compost bins! Any of these locations are ideal as they are well away from other city dwellers.

Before putting your hive in place at ground level, it pays to lay a few paving slabs. Ventilation of the hive is very important, so placing it on slabs will prevent grass and weeds growing under it and hindering the flow of air. I was concerned that my chosen spot for two of my hives was on the edge of a lawn, which I regularly cut with a tractor mower. At first I drove by quickly within a foot or two of the hive, but I've found that the bees pay no attention to me or the lawnmower.

Perhaps your own garden or property is not an ideal location to keep bees. Farmers, horticulturists or allotment gardeners rely on bees to pollinate their crops and many would be only too pleased to have bees on their land. So, if you are struggling for a location on your own property, ask around: you will probably find someone to help you locate your hives.

Your local association may also have a list of property owners who have offered their land for hives.

An orchard is an ideal location. Apple, cherry, plum and pear trees are all great sources of pollen for your bees when they are in blossom and fruit growers need pollination to get a good harvest. Commercial beekeepers around the world transfer their hives to pollen sources throughout a season. In Britain, beekeepers transfer hives to the moors when heather is in flower and beekeepers in the USA transfer them from almond orchards to orange groves.

It's probably unwise to place your hives where there is easy public access. Unfortunately there are idiots who take pleasure in throwing rocks at hives to knock them over. There have also been reports of hives being stolen. So, when looking for a location, try not to choose a place that's too visible from the road or where the general public have too easy an access.

Hints & tips

- Place hives on solid slabs to aid ventilation

Opposite: A tractor lawnmower passing close to hives in a garden

Above: Picking apples in an orchard in Kent

Getting your Bees and transferring them

"Where to get them"

Once you've got the necessary equipment together, the next thing is finding where to get your first bees. There are three possible solutions: a nucleus of bees, a colony, or collecting a swarm.

A nucleus is the best option for a new beekeeper, as taking a full colony or capturing a swarm might be overly daunting in your first year. I started with three hives, two of which were started from a nucleus.

A nucleus is really a half colony, consisting of five to six frames of bees, brood, eggs and larvae with a queen. Basically it's a box, in which the frames sit, that has air vents and an entrance hole.

You can buy a nucleus of bees from most bee equipment retailers or local beekeepers. Your local association will know which of their members have nucleuses to sell. Nucleuses are generally for sale from May and throughout the summer. Earlier ones will have a previous year's queen. Later ones should have a current year queen and

will only become available once the newly reared virgin queen has mated.

Having sourced your first nucleus, be prepared well in advance of its arrival. You will be given an approximate date, but this is flexible due to when the virgin queens mate. Once you get the call to tell you its ready, you may need to collect it, or it may be delivered. It's best to get it in the evening after any foraging bees have returned for the night. Make sure your hive

Hints & tips

- Ask your local association for members who sell nucleuses of bees.

A nucleus of bees in a travel box in place on a hive stand

stand is in your chosen position before you receive the hive. When you get the nucleus, place the nucleus box on the hive stand and open the entrance hole. The bees might sound a bit agitated, but this is normal, as they have travelled in a sealed box. Leave the box for a minimum of 24 hours and the bees will settle. The following morning the foraging bees will start to exit the nucleus to get their bearings in their new location. When you are ready to transfer your nucleus into your hive, light your smoker, put on your bee suit, have your hive tool in your hand, an empty super, and a feeder with some 1:1 sugar solution ready.

Lift the nucleus box off the hive stand and stand beside it. Put the wire mesh floor in place on top of the hive stand with an entrance block and an empty brood box.

If your nucleus comprises five frames, and your hive will take eleven, place three frames of new wax foundation at the furthest point of the hive away from you.

Open the lid of the nucleus and give a little smoke over the tops of the frames. Remove the first frame with bees on. It may be stuck down with propolis, but you can easily dislodge it with your hive tool.

61

Place the first frame in your hive next to a frame of foundation. Continue lifting out and placing the frames in your hive, placing them in exactly the same order as they were in the nucleus. These frames will end up being central in your hive.

You should now have five frames of bees and three frames of foundation. Gently nudge the frames together with your hive tool so they fit across the hive from the far end. There will be a gap nearest to you, in which you place three more frames of wax foundation and finally fit your dummy board.

You will now see your brood box is full of frames all parallel to each other with the five frames from the nucleus central in your hive. When you are happy that all the frames are in place, check the inside of the nucleus box as many bees will still be clinging on.

Lift the nucleus box over the hive, and with a shake or two, dislodge these bees onto the tops of the frames. Many will fall, but not all. To get the rest into the hive, place the box against the hive entrance and as evening falls the remaining bees will find their way into the hive to join the others.

Close the hive giving a few puffs of smoke over the tops of the frames to encourage the bees to go down into it. Then place the crown board, with the holes covered, diagonally on top of the brood box and wiggle it into place to dislodge any bees so you don't crush them.

Wait until evening to give the bees some feed, so you don't excite them or invite robbing bees. Uncover one of the holes on the crown board and place your feeder over it. Fill the feeder with the 1:1 sugar solution. Drip a little solution onto the frames, through the feeder hole, so your bees

know the feed is there. Cover the feeder when you've done this.

The roof will not fit with the feeder in place due to its height, so you have to place an empty super on top before replacing the roof. To avoid trapping bees in the roof, give them a bit of smoke or use your bee brush to wipe them away, and then fit the roof. You now have your first colony of bees.

You will need to keep a daily eye on the feed, depending on the weather conditions. If conditions are warm the bees will be out foraging, so the feeder will only be needed for a few days. Keep topping up the feeder: the bees will stop taking it down when they have had enough. You can remove the feeder and empty super when they have stopped taking the sugar solution.

Opposite: Inspecting frames of bees from a nucleus

Above: Bees clustered around entrance after a hive inspection

Opening the hive

"Your first inspection"

You've had your nucleus of bees for two weeks and it's time to do your first hive inspection. As a new beekeeper you will be itching to do this, but be patient and give your bees this period of time to settle in. Within a day of hiving your bees you will see them in flight around the hive, and foraging bees returning with pollen on their legs. If this is the case, then the queen is laying eggs to produce young and therefore increasing the size of the colony.

Choose a fine day for your inspection and try to do it near the middle of the day if you can, when many of the foraging bees will be out. Put your bee suit on, and before pulling up the veil and zipping it in place, light the smoker and ensure it's smoking well.

Once you have everything you need, and you're covered up, you can give the hive entrance a few puffs of smoke. Wait a couple of minutes, then remove the roof, laying it alongside the hive with the top of the roof to the ground.

Having it in this position gives you somewhere to place frames as you work. Run the sharp end of your hive tool round the crown board cracking the propolis that the bees have deposited. Sometimes it can be quite hard to get the crown board to release and other times it comes away easily.

Once it's free, lift it off and inspect the underside. You will see bees clinging to it, but you are checking that the queen is not there. It's unlikely,

but it's better to be safe as you don't want her to drop onto the ground. Now place the crown board on the ground leaning it against the hive entrance.

You will see the open hive now with the frames lined up across its width. Some bees will be flying but there shouldn't be too many airborne around you. You will see bees on the frame top bars, so you can give a few puffs of smoke across the tops of the frames to keep them occupied. Don't blow the smoke down into the hive: it only needs a few puffs over the top.

Stand to the side of your hive with the frames going away from you, and using your hive tool, gently remove the dummy board. This should be the frame closest to you. Again check for the queen before standing the dummy board in the roof in a position that matches the layout of your hive.

Lifting off the crown board

A few puffs of smoke over the tops of the frames

Now you are going to remove the first frame. Lever it out, and as this is your first inspection, you should just see a frame of wax foundation. Place this alongside the dummy board in the hive roof.

Next remove the following frame which should be similar, or you may see that some of the wax foundation has been drawn out and the bees have started to create their comb. Place this in the roof also. Don't worry about the few bees on these frames: they'll find their way back.

The reason for placing a few frames in the roof is to give yourself working space as you go through each one in the hive. You can now work through, lifting out each frame to inspect it.

The further you go into the hive, the more bees you will find covering the frames. Removing some of these bees will help you see the comb better. To do this, hold each end of the frame and place it over and slightly into the gap you've removed it from. Give it one or two firm downward shakes. This will dislodge many of the bees and they will fall, totally unharmed, into the bottom of the hive.

If you find your bees are now a bit more agitated, give them a few more puffs of smoke over the hive to calm them down.

It's always handy to have a cloth ready in case you feel your bees are a bit too agitated or if you feel uncomfortable. If this is the case, cover the hive with the cloth and walk away. They will soon settle down and you can then return to complete your inspection.

Continue your inspection, checking the next frame and placing it back in the hive against the outer wall nearest to you. You will see that now you've created a space in the hive, it's much easier for you to handle each individual frame.

You will now have reached the frames you placed in the hive from your nucleus. Inspect each one, shaking off the bees, and you should be able to spot eggs and larvae. You'll find it's easier to spot them if you can place yourself so that the sun is over your shoulder, lighting the inside of the cells.

Keep going through all the frames and you should be able to spot pollen and nectar cells, and as you reach the central frames, the sealed brood. You will also notice stored honey, which has been capped with a white creamy coloured wax, along the top portion of the frame.

Opposite: Placing the crown board against the front of the hive

Above right: Lifting out a frame to inspect it for brood and eggs

Hints & tips

- Do not stand in front of the hive blocking the flight path: your bees won't like it.

- Check each frame to see if you can spot the queen.

- Hold frames over the hive. If they are heavy you can rest a corner on another frame bar.

Don't worry if you do not spot the queen: she will be busy laying eggs and tends to hide away from the light. With most purchased nucleuses, the queen will be marked by a colour paint mark on her thorax. It is often colour coded to indicate the year she was born.

If you do spot her, you will see that she is larger and definitely stands out from the crowd.
The reason for your first inspection is to check that the queen is laying. So if you can see eggs, larvae and sealed brood then all is well.

Once you've gone through all the frames you can ease them back into their original position until you have a space nearest to you from where the two frames and dummy board were removed.

Replace the frames you stored in the roof in the same position and orientation in which you found them and then add the dummy board.

When all the frames are back in the hive you can nudge them into place using your hive tool and you are ready to close up the hive. Give the edges of the hive a quick smoke to remove any bees and place the crown board at an angle across the top. Then gently wiggle the crown board into place. Occasionally you will crush the odd bee but this will stop you from crushing too many. Make certain the crown board holes are covered, clear any bees from the top with a bit of smoke, and put the roof on. You have now completed your first inspection.

Keeping notes

It's a good idea to keep notes on each of your hives. I keep a card in the roof of each hive which enables me to make quick written notes after each inspection. I then keep more comprehensive notes taken from the cards and enter the details onto a computer spreadsheet.

Keeping notes will give you a history of the hive, its activities and your actions over the years. For me, a good example of this, was seeing an unmarked queen in one of my hives at the beginning of the season.

I marked her with a dab of white marker. However, I was certain that when I had seen the queen the season before she was marked green. By going back through my notes, I was able to see that I was correct. Therefore the colony had superseded her either late in the season the previous year or early in the current season.

Making notes of the numbers of brood sides and honey stores will enable you to gauge how strong or weak a colony is, the exact dates when honey was extracted, or when medication was given to treat for varroa. These are just some of the many examples of why making notes is good practice.

Hive Card

Hive No. 3

Date	Notes
23ʳᵈ March 2010	4 sides brood Condition excellent – Spring Clean
11th April 2010	12 sides brood – 1st Drone cells Condition excellent
17th April 2010	14 sides brood Added ½ brood box + super
23rd April 2010	17 sides brood – marked Queen/white Honey in super – none capped excellent condition
30th April 2010	18 + 10 sides brood Queen cell larva Frame 9
1st May 2010	12 + sides Honey uncapped Created Artificial Swarm New Hive No. 5

Above: Frame showing empty cells awaiting an egg, uncapped larvae and sealed honey at the top of the frame

Above: Frame showing cells with different coloured pollen, stored nectar cells and sealed honey

Above: Frame showing sealed brood

Above: Close-up of larvae cells

Queen marking

Marking the queen will help you to locate her within the brood box, especially when it comes to splitting a hive to prevent swarming. There are a number of tools to help you capture or hold her whilst you mark her.

I use a queen cage, which is placed over her and carefully pressed into the comb. Worker bees can escape through the spiked cage. Gently press down, being careful not to crush her, while you place a coloured mark on her thorax using a special marker pen, available in a variety of colours from bee equipment suppliers.

As a hobby beekeeper I mark all my queens with a white marker, as I find white stands out better. Commercial beekeepers will use colour-coded markers to enable them to identify the year a queen was hatched.

Above: A queen cage.

Opposite: A marked queen stands out amongst the other bees.

Queen yearly colour codes

Year Ending	Colour
1 or 6	White
2 or 7	Yellow
3 or 8	Red
4 or 9	Green
5 or 0	Blue

Hygiene

Hygiene around your hives is very important. Safe practice would be to use one hive tool per hive, however this is not practical, so always clean your hive tool after each inspection.

Fill a bucket with a solution of hot water and soda crystals and drop your hive tool into it. Then, before you put it away, scrape it with a wire scrubber to remove any propolis.

It is important to be as clean as possible around your own hives, but it's even more important should you visit another beekeeper's apiary. Don't use your own tools: ask if they have a spare hive tool if you need to use one.

Leather gloves need to be cleaned regularly, and bee suits occasionally. I soak my gloves over-night in hot water and soda crystals. The propolis on the fingers cracks off but will always leave the leather stained. Leather gloves take an age to dry and will become stiff, but they are not difficult to get back to their pliable best. Many beekeepers use bare hands or disposable surgical gloves, which is the most hygienic method.

WARNING: Some beekeepers will not allow leather gloves in their apiary, so check first.

Feeding bees

"If you take their honey you have to return something"

Bees are intelligent creatures and know they have to store food to survive the winter months. As beekeepers we remove some of their winter honey stores and so need to substitute it. We can also help them by supplementing their feed in harsh times as and when they need it. Knowing how and when to feed your bees is very important to maintain a strong colony.

Spring feed

At the first signs of spring, your bees will be out foraging for the first pollen and nectar of the year. As these first supplies come in, the bees' natural instinct is to increase the size of the colony and the queen will start laying eggs. However, your bees' stock of food within the hive will be at its lowest and this is now the time you may need to help the colony.

They have survived the winter so you do not want them to die due to the lack of food now. If you feel food stocks are low, prepare a 2:1 sugar solution and give it to the bees by rapid or contact feeder. You may have to keep topping up the feeder for a couple of weeks until nectar is in full flow. You can't give them too much: once they have taken all they need they will stop and you can remove the feeder.

Spring can be a dangerous time for the colony in temperate climates. It may be warm for a few days then the weather can very quickly become cold and wet again. Your bees will have started collecting pollen and nectar to feed the new larvae. A cold spell will halt new flower growth and because the bees can't forage, their stock of food dwindles further. Again, this is the time to add a feeder and give them a strong 2:1 sugar solution to see them through.

Your hive management and observation skills are needed at this time of year. Regular hefting of the hives, observing bee movements and the weather, will all help you to determine whether they need feeding. Feed them if you are uncertain, as they will only take the feed if they need it.

Some areas of the UK can experience what is known as the 'June gap'. This is a two-week period between the end of spring and the start of the summer plants coming into flower, during which pollen and nectar sources dry up. This is another potentially risky time for your bees and you will need to keep an eye on them to see they do not starve.

A rapid feeder on a hive. Bees can be seen in the central aperture collecting the sugar solution.
Note an empty super is on the hive to allow the roof to fit when a feeder is in place.

Feeding a nucleus or swarm

If you have taken delivery of a nucleus of bees, or have managed to collect a swarm, feeding will help to get them started and settled in your hive.

Once transferred to a hive, a nucleus has very little feed on the frames and a swarm will go into a new hive without any honey stores. Your hive will have frames of new wax foundation, and we can help our bees draw this out to create their own comb.

Prepare a 1:1 sugar solution and feed the hive. As with other feeding, they will take only what they need.

Autumn feed

When you have harvested the honey from the supers and given the hive its varroa mite treatment, it's time to feed the colony so it has plenty of food stores for the winter. This feeding needs to take place whilst it is still relatively warm (15 degrees C/59f) so that the bees can evaporate the water content to enable them to store it. Each hive will need a minimum of 18 kg (40 lbs) of winter stores.

Prepare a 2:1 sugar solution and feed the hive with a rapid or contact feeder. You will be surprised how much and how quickly the bees will take this solution, but keep feeding them until they stop taking it.

As you make your final inspection before winter, you need to make sure the frames are full of stores. As with honey, the bees will cap the stored cells with a white wax and they will look the same as stored honey.

I only give each of my hives about 7 kg (15lbs) of solution because my bees have an abundance of ivy pollen and nectar close by in the autumn which they use to build up their stores.

You might find there are plenty late flowering plants, such as ivy, in your location and your bees will use these to build up their stocks. You have to use your own judgement and you will be able to judge from your inspections when the colony has ample food stocks.

Once you are satisfied the required stores are in place, the feeder can be removed and you can make your final winter preparations.

There are numerous types of feeder on the market and with time you might experiment with a few. Perhaps the most important aspect for the novice at this stage is the feeder's volume. If your hive is at the bottom of the garden it will be possible to refill the feeder each day as needed. However if your hive is some distance from your home, then a larger feeder that holds a larger supply, might be a better option. It is known that bees can consume a gallon (4.54 litres) of sugar solution in two to three days.

Winter feed

Half way through winter, you need to check that the colony's supply of food has not reduced too much. Hefting the hive will give you a good indication. You can supplement the store if you feel food stocks are running low.

Fondant icing sugar is available from bee equipment suppliers or you can get packs of it from your local supermarket. When feeding your bees with fondant, try and wait for a relatively warmer day, hopefully with some sun on the hive.

You need to work quickly, as opening the hive releases the heat the colony has created when clustered together. Place the fondant package directly onto the frames over the cluster, adding an eke for spacing and closing the hive again. This should take you no more than 30 seconds. You can check the fondant in a month's time and replenish if it has been eaten.

Water

One often overlooked fact is that bees need a supply of drinking water. I am lucky enough to have a water-filled ditch close to some of my hives and I also see bees collecting water from a pond in a whisky barrel on my terrace.

As bees cannot swim it is essential you give them a floating platform to land on whilst they take in water. Aquatic plants, twigs, or even leaves floating on the surface will suffice. Although I see my bees on fresh water, I've been told bees prefer stagnant water, so don't worry if your water source doesn't look too appetising to you.

Above: A rapid feeder in place under the empty super.

Opposite: Honey bee collecting moisture from plant leaves in a garden pond

Placing a contact feeder on to a plastic omlet hive

Making up sugar solution

Sugar syrup solutions are either 2:1 or 1:1 mixtures of sugar and water. I've found the simplest method is to measure it out by volume. A one-kilo(2.2lbs) bag of sugar will fill a ½ litre/1 pint Pyrex kitchen jug twice to produce a 2:1 mix. One jug of sugar to one jug of water makes a 1:1 solution mix. Of course you will need to make it in greater quantities, so simply multiply these measures depending how much solution you need.

As a guide for how much 2:1 winter feed to use, it's recommended that each hive needs 18 kg (40 lbs) of stores to see the colony through the winter.

0.5 litres (1 pint) of water weighs about 0.6 kg (1.25lbs).

1kg (2.2 lbs) of sugar added with 0.5litres (1 pint) will weigh 1.6 kg (2.45 lbs).

Sugar solution measurements

- **1:1 Sugar Solution** — 1lb sugar / 1 pint water
  0.5kg sugar / 0.5 litres water

- **2:1 Sugar Solution** — 2lb sugar / 1 pint water
  1kg sugar / 0.5 litres water

1kg = 2.2 lb	1 litre = 0.76 pint
2kg = 4.4 lb	2 litres = 3.52 pint
5kg = 11 lb	5 litres = 8.80 pint
10kg = 22 lb	10 litres = 17.6 pint
1lb = 0.5 kg	1 pint = 0.568 litres
2lb = 0.9 kg	2 pints = 1.136 litres
5lb = 2.3 kg	5 pints = 2.84 litres
10lb = 4.5 kg	10 pints = 5.68 litres

Notice the position of the capped honey is close to the brood

I bought a large jam-making pot to mix the syrup in. I've found it ideal for diluting the sugar granules into the syrup solution. Slowly heat the sugar, stirring regularly until all it has been diluted. Allow it to cool before funnelling into 2-litre plastic fizzy drink bottles. They are ideal for pouring the sugar solution into the feeder when it's in place on the hive.

See Chapter on Wintering your bees.

Having done your final extraction of the year, you will not know the weight of stored food still in the hive. So keep feeding until your bees stop taking the sugar syrup down, then heft the hive to feel its weight.

To complicate matters you may come across various mixing formulas devised by experts, which may indicate that my volume measurements are not correct. However, in my short period of

keeping bees, I've used the calculations above and have found that the bees happily take the syrup down and store it for winter. Also come spring, when I first open my hives, I have never lost a colony.

Hints & tips

- A good indicator is, that if the hive feels as though it's nailed to floor, it has sufficient food stores. However, this is only an indication: not an exact science. Food store positioning is equally important.

- In early spring the position of the bees' food is very important – feed if necessary.

Subsequent inspections

"Adding Supers"

Regular hive inspections are necessary for the welfare of your bees. During spring you should inspect your hives every seven to nine days. Generally, you are checking your hive to see if the queen is laying eggs successfully and that your bees are not running out of space.

Also during this period, queen cells can be found and you may need to take preventative measures to stop the colony swarming. Inspections can be less frequent in the summer after the swarming period as long as you have allowed for the colony numbers to expand with supers in place.

You need to go through each frame following the same procedure as your first inspection. As time progresses you will see that all the frames are drawn out and the comb the bees have built are filled either with eggs, larvae or capped brood. Other frames will have cells full of pollen and nectar, some capped and others waiting to be capped. You will also see sealed honey in the top portion of the frames.

You'll need to check for queen cells too. You are unlikely to see queen cells hanging from the bottom of the frames if you have taken delivery of your nucleus late in the season. However, you

could see them appearing if you received your nucleus earlier. If this happens in your first year, it is advisable to crush or cut out the queen cells, as you don't want your colony to produce a new queen and swarm.

If you have received your nucleus from a reputable supplier, you should find them clean of any varroa mite or other bee diseases. But you need to keep an eye open whilst going through your hive frame by frame.

It's highly unlikely, but check to see if any of your bees have varroa mites clinging to their backs. One or two aren't a problem, but if you see any more, get advice from an experienced beekeeper as you might need to treat them immediately to stop the mite increasing.

Also check the mite board under the wire mesh floor because debris will fall through as the bees

clean the hive. Look for any dead mites. Look also for the fungal disease, chalk brood whose spores are ingested by the larvae and germinate in the gut thus killing it.

The larvae are mummified and look like a cell filled with chalk. The house bees will eject these from the hive, but if you see the occasional one, you can help by removing it. Chalk brood is seasonal and seldom a problem, but speak to an experienced beekeeper if you see more than the odd one or two cells.

Wax moth is another problem which first year beekeepers might encounter. Again you are unlikely to see a major infestation, but if you do see the occasional one, remove it. Look out for a silk trail over the sealed brood, smaller but similar to that left by a garden snail. I was given the following tip to help me find the wax moth larva after spotting silk trails: tap the frame with your hive tool a few times. This encourages the larva to appear from the cell allowing you to pinch it out.

Although any of the above are unlikely to be a major problem in your first year, it's better to be aware of them should they occur in the future.

At this stage in beekeeping, the most important check is to make sure your bees have plenty of

space. If the weather has been favourable, the queen will have been laying constantly. These new eggs will hatch in 21 days, so the colony will be expanding rapidly. The colony needs space for the queen to lay her eggs and to store pollen and nectar, so we want to encourage the bees to expand and store honey for us to harvest.

Once you see the outer frames have had their wax foundation drawn out, it's time to give them the extra space, and you can't do it too early.

To give your bees more space, you need to add a super above the brood box. Adding a super is a simple and quick process. With the hive open, place a queen excluder onto the brood box. A puff of smoke over the top will clear the bees as you sit the queen excluder on top with the slots at right angles to the frames.

Add a super with the frames full of wax foundation on top of this and place in the same direction as those in the brood box. Then replace the crown board onto the super followed by the roof.

The bees will soon discover this extra space and will move up through the queen excluder, drawing out the wax foundation and creating comb to store honey in. With the queen excluder in place, only worker bees can enter and return from the super. So, as the food stores can now be placed above, the laying queen will have further space in which to lay her eggs.

A strong colony can fill a super within a week during the height of the pollen and nectar season. Keep a close eye on your hive, adding further supers as they are needed. It is not unheard of for a hive to have four or five supers in place by the end of the season. If you're going to miss a weekly inspection because you're going away, adding two supers at once will safeguard any rapid expansion during this period.

This method of adding new supers on top of each other is known as 'top supering'. Some beekeepers prefer bottom supering i.e. adding any new supers below those in place. This creates more work as you have to lift off the existing supers to add new ones below.

The prime reason for bottom supering is to put space next to the brood chamber. This offers the bees more immediate room since the main reason for swarming is lack of space. However, some believe this method also encourages more honey to be stored, as the bees have to travel less distance through the hive to store it.

If you are hoping to have some comb honey, it pays to have the super with the un-wired frames at the top of the hive. Bees feet do get dirty and the more they pass over the comb the dirtier it will get. As time passes you will notice how dark the brood comb gets and in your third year you will be exchanging frames for new frames of foundation in the brood box.

Placing the supers to collect any comb honey at the very top of the hive will keep the wax capping brilliantly white and perfect when it's cut out and offered as natural comb honey.

I found with some of my hives, that the queen was laying eggs so rapidly that space for brood was running out within the brood box. If you find this, you can increase the size of the brood box by placing a super on it but without a queen excluder between it.

The queen excluder can then be placed on top of the super before you add further ones. By doing this you are basically creating one and half brood boxes, therefore giving the queen ample space to lay her eggs in.

Hints & tips

- Your local association will have a course on diseases. Do go on one, as it will enable you to recognise diseases and pests when you do inspections.

- A golden rule – if you see bees on six to seven frames in a super, add another one.

Wintering your bees

Give them a little help

Having nurtured your bees through summer, your preparation for the winter months is very important if they are to survive into the spring. In the UK, you must start preparing your bees for winter by the end of August or early September. Countries with diverse climates will start their preparations at different times.

When you've harvested the honey it's time to treat and protect the hive against varroa mite. You can buy a number of veterinary approved treatments from bee equipment suppliers. I've used a thymol-based treatment called Apiguard.

If this is your chosen method, you will need two 50g trays per hive. Place one tray, opened onto the brood frames, in a corner of your hive for 10 to 14 days. You won't be able to replace the crown board with the trays in place, so use an eke as a spacer. Or if you don't have one, use an empty super.

When you inspect the hive at the end of this period, you should find that the bees have taken the gel down into the hive. Replace this tray

Research

New treatments come onto the market regularly, so read and follow annual recommendations from your national or local association, and in the beekeeping press.

Left: Apiguard tray on frames in the hive

Opposite: A Hive in the garden with snow falling

with a new one and leave for the same period. This treatment will keep the level of infestation to a minimum and should be applied primarily at the end of the summer. It can be applied at other times during in the season as appropriate and so long as the supers storing honey are not in use. Always read the manufacturer's guidelines for any chemical treatments you apply to your hives.

Once the varroa treatment has been applied it's time to feed your bees. This enables them to build up a stock of food to last them through the winter. This should be done immediately as the outside temperature still needs to be warm (over 15 degrees C/59F) enough to enable the bees to reduce the water content to allow them to store the sugar in the comb cells.

You will need to mix a 2:1 sugar solution in preparation for feeding your bees. To feed them you only have to remove the roof and open one of the holes in your crown board, placing the feeder over this hole.

Once it's in place, fill the feeder with the sugar solution and drip a little through the hole onto the frames to let the bees know there is feed for them.

Replace the feeder cover, add an empty super as a spacer, and replace the hive roof. You'll be surprised how much and how quickly the bees will take down the sugar solution, and you'll find you'll need to check the level daily or every other day.

When refilling your rapid feeder, you will see the bees in the central aperture feeding on the solution. Slowly pour the sugar syrup into the feeder so you don't drown the bees as the syrup level rises.

The bees will move as you refill. However some will get immersed in it and you'll think they have drowned. Bees have a system to create an air pocket round them - this silver lining is visible. If they are not too deep into the syrup solution, they will slowly rise and extract themselves.

At times, you may also find the sugar solution has crystallised, preventing the bees getting to the syrup. If this happens, remove the feeder, cover the hole in the crown board and wash the feeder in hot water. You can then return it to the hive and refill it with the sugar solution.

Your bees will need plenty of food to survive the winter, so continue feeding them; they will stop taking any more of the solution down once they have all they need.

A minimum of 18kg (40 pounds) of stored honey is the recommended amount necessary for a colony to survive winter. Try lifting a corner of the hive off the ground (hefting) to give yourself a good indication of how much food is in there. If it feels as though the hive is nailed to the ground, it's a good indication that it is full of food.

Hefting is also a good method to judge how much food is still in the hive throughout the winter months. If the hive becomes light, then you will know that food is getting short and may need your attention.

At the end of August and during September, you will often see many wasps attracted to your hives. As ripe fruit falls from trees, wasps seem to be in abundance as they gorge themselves.

I have seen wasps attempting to gain entry into my hives and seen them attacked by the entrance guards. If this is a problem you may need to reduce the entrance to a single bee space. You can purchase glass wasp catching

Opposite: A hive prepared for winter with ratchet strap and garden netting in place

jars very cheaply, or even use an old jar with a small amount of orange juice or jam in it. I place a wasp jar on each hive and catch hundreds of wasps over this period. This is far more preferable than allowing the robbing wasps to enter the hive and steal stores.

With your feeding complete, there are a few more jobs you need to carry out. First remove the mite board below the wire mesh floor. This will allow fresh air to circulate throughout the hive and it can remain off throughout winter.

To allow further ventilation, uncover the holes on your crown board and cover with a tight wire mesh, or as I have done, loosely cover the holes with hessian sacking. Keeping the hive well ventilated in this way is important because, while bees can withstand the cold when clustered together, a build-up of moisture can cause problems.

The entrance to the hive needs to be reduced and many beekeepers fit a mouse guard. In cold winters, mice will find your hive a comfortable home and the guard prevents them entering through the narrow holes. Experts have recently said that mouse guards are not necessary, as a standard restricted entrance block is small enough to prevent small rodents entering.

If your hives are in an open windy location, or near large trees as mine are, place ratchet straps around them. In high winds or if something falls onto a hive, the straps will keep the hive parts together.

During a long period of frosty weather, woodpeckers can be a problem. If they are unable to feed themselves, a hive is an attractive alternative and they have been known to create a large hole in the hive wall, through which they eat the bees.

To prevent this, I encase each hive in wire garden netting, just pinning it into place. Depending where you are, you might have other predators that might show an interest in your hives. If you do, seek local advice on the best way to protect them.

When you have completed all these tasks, you can leave your bees in peace throughout the winter months.

When you have completed your winter preparations in September and early October, clean and store your equipment away in a dry place. Your supers, drawn frames and queen excluders can be scraped with your hive tool to remove excess wax and propolis.

Wax moth can be attracted to your stored frames, so it's advisable to take steps to prevent this. I was advised to place the supers on blocks to aid ventilation, and as you stack your supers on top of each other, place a sheet of newspaper between each one and drip some lavender oil onto it. I understand that the scent of lavender will keep wax moth at bay.

To prevent mice getting in, place a queen excluder below the lowest and on top of the highest super. If a mouse does get into your stored comb frames, it will destroy all the hard work your bees have done to produce it.

Hints & tips

- The best time to clean equipment to remove propolis is when it is cold and frosty.

Hessian covering holes on the crown board

Placing fondant on the frames to feed the bees NB Notice the eke in place.

Dead bees outside the hive on a sunny day in February

Supers and nucleus boxes stored away for winter

The frames of comb in your supers are precious, so you need to protect them for your bees. Come the following season, when you return the supers to the hive, the bees will be able to store honey in the comb immediately without having to produce it from new wax foundation. You will have helped to reduce their work and you'll gain a month's worth of honey storage because they won't have to put effort into building comb.

I suggest cleaning frames and supers before stacking them for winter. However, as the outside temperature will still be relatively warm, removing the sticky propolis isn't easy. I remove the worst and then stack.

The easiest time to clean frames and supers is during a period of frost. So if frost is forecast, place your supers outside overnight and work on them the next day. The once sticky propolis is now brittle and cracks off easily when scrapped with your hive tool.

Cleaning frames on a frosty morning

Over winter, the colony will have been reduced to about 10,000 bees. The drones will have been ejected and only the late hatched bees will be in the hive with the queen. Clustered together, they will maintain the hive temperature, seeing out the winter months.

Keep a general eye on your hives during winter, especially after strong winds or heavy rain. You might find on a warmer sunny day that some bees are out stretching their wings. It's a welcome sight to see them flying around the entrance as it indicates they are surviving the winter well.

Don't be alarmed, if on a sunny day, you see a few dead bees on the landing board or outside the hive. Some bees will die during the winter months, and as they like to keep their home clean, they will dispose of any dead bees when it's warm enough for them to do so. They will have all disappeared by the next day, because the birds in your garden will be happy to receive this free meal.

You will need to check monthly throughout winter that the feed stores are holding out. A quick visit to your hives and hefting will tell you by their weight how much food is still in the hive.

Stores may be starting to deplete by February and you may need to give a little help. If this is the case, and if you can find a reasonably warm day with some sunshine on your hive, you can give your bees a fondant feed.

You'll find fondant icing, used to ice cakes, in all supermarkets, as well in bee equipment suppliers. Wrap the fondant package in cling film to prevent it drying out too quickly and cut a strip out of one side of the packaging.

Remove the hive roof and crown board placing the fondant, with the cut hole side down, onto the frames where there is the largest concentration of bees. Work quickly, as you want to complete this task without losing too much of the heat from the hive.

Once the feed is in place, you'll need to fit an eke before fitting the crown board and roof. This high concentrated sugar feed will help the bees to survive until spring. However, check regularly to see if they need more. Feed them as required until spring arrives and you see the bees bringing in new nectar and pollen.

Strong healthy colonies
are those prepared well in
spring and autumn.

Collecting swarms

"a free colony"

As I mentioned at the beginning of this book, I started with three hives, two of which came from nucleuses.

Above: Bees having swarmed and clustered on the trunk of an apple tree

I was able to colonise my third hive with a swarm that I collected. As novices, many of you may have no intention of going anywhere near a swarm of bees at this stage. However, if you are either brave, or perhaps foolhardy like me, or maybe a bit of both, then a swarm is an excellent way to get yourself a free colony.

Collecting and hiving a swarm the first few times is stressful but exciting. I think, if they get the opportunity, every beekeeper should see this spectacle even if they're not actively involved in the collection.

It is in the nature of bees to swarm. Some do have more of a tendency to do so than others, but one of the triggers is lack of space. Losing half your colony will reduce the amount of honey you will harvest later in the year, so all beekeepers work towards swarm prevention.

However, there are occasions that a swarm is lost, and it happens to the most experienced

beekeepers. This is not particularly good news
if it's your hive that's swarmed, but it's handy for
the person who has the opportunity to collect it.

When bees are preparing to swarm, usually
during May, June and into July, they engorge
three days worth of honey stores.

It's one of nature's spectacles to see thousands
of bees departing a hive or their nest in the wild.
It's as if a tap has been opened with bees pouring
out and filling the sky. The sound of thousands
of buzzing airborne bees looking for a place to
settle is intimidating and unless you're covered,
it's best to keep your distance.

Above: Hiving a swarm using a white
sheet and ramp to enable bees to
climb up into the hive

'A swarm in May
is worth a load of hay;

a swarm in June
is worth a silver spoon;

but a swarm in July
is not worth a fly'

For it is then too late,
to store up honey before
the flowers begin to fade.

Wild Life in Southern County
R. Jefferies 1879

Nucleus box tied above swarm cluster and
beekeeper smoking the bees into the box

Soon after leaving their home, the bees will
settle as a large cluster on a branch, a gate
post, or even on a piece of machinery. Often
this cluster will resemble a large rugby ball in
shape and is usually within 50-metres of their
original home.

Once they have clustered together, surrounding
the queen, the scouts will be out searching for a
new home. This can take from one hour to three
days. Once a new home has been found the
colony will fly again and enter their new home to
continue their breeding cycle.

Collecting a swarm can only be done when it's
in a cluster and in an accessible position. Don't

attempt to collect one if its position is going to
put you in any danger: it is not worth the risk.

If you do want to colonise one of your hives,
you will need to put the word out that you
are interested in a swarm. I had spoken to a
commercial gardener who phoned me to tell me
he had seen swarms on two properties where he
was working.

If you get a call from someone who spots a
swarm, you'll have to drop everything as the bees
could soon move on. If you are aiming to collect
a swarm, have everything you need ready in
advance so you can quickly put it in your car and
be off at a moment's notice.

The crucial items you will need are:

- a skep or good size cardboard box (12 bottle wine box is ideal) with the bottom securely taped
- a white sheet
- secateurs
- your smoker
- protective clothing.

My first swarm was a small colony some 15 feet high on the outside eave of a bungalow. I think they had been there a while as they had built some comb. I was successful in cutting them down, getting them into a nucleus box, then hiving them.

Unfortunately after two days they left the hive. I found out later that it was probably because I hadn't put a feeder on immediately to help them draw out the wax foundation in the frames. Although I hadn't been entirely successful, I'd learnt a lot and was now more prepared should I get another call.

Fortunately this came two weeks later. My friendly gardener called to say he was working in a garden preparing it for a wedding reception that was being held in a marquee. Naturally the bride and family were very concerned that they had thousands of bees flying about and didn't want this to happen during the reception.

By the time I arrived the bees had disappeared: no sight or sound of them. We searched the garden and eventually found them about 10 feet up clustered in a large laurel bush. They were very calm, and as I had hoped, accessible. This time I had brought a hive with me. I was glad I had because the colony would not have fitted into a nucleus box.

I positioned the hive on the grass, about 10 paces from the swarm. I had a hive stand on short legs in place, brood box with frames, crown board and a roof. I laid a piece of board from the ground to the hive entrance and covered it with a white sheet. My aim was to get the swarm onto the sheet because I had learnt from my research that the bees would follow the queen into the hive.

With the hive ready, I lit my smoker and dressed in my bee suit. Fortunately I had brought my wife's suit with me, which I gave to the gardener. We discussed our plan of action for how we were going to collect the swarm. With beating hearts we began to put it into action.

I had decided against smoking the cluster as I felt this might agitate them. Firstly, we cut out a few of the lower branches to give us working room and easier access.

The bees were clustered mainly on one vertical branch and another less thick one. We decided I would stand on a stepladder holding the main branch whilst the gardener slowly, without too much vibration, sawed through the branch lower down. I clung on nervously, expecting a cloud of bees to suddenly explode into the air.

Once he had cut half way through the branch, he passed me some branch loppers and I carefully cut the thinner branch, which was

Hints & tips

- Some experts say don't feed a swarm for two days so they use up the engorged honey in their stomachs rather than storing it.

partly holding the cluster. It held its position as I cut, without falling and taking bees with it. We were concerned that once the main branch was cut through, I wouldn't be able to keep it vertical and it would fall sideways. Luckily with the final cut, I was able to hold it and was surprised that the branch and the cluster of bees weren't heavier. Once I had hold of it, I slowly made my way down the stepladder and carried the branch, still vertical, towards the hive.

Ten members of the wedding party were watching my every move. I suggested they should retreat a bit further, as soon there would be lot of agitated bees in the air.

Once I was by the hive, I lowered the branch and swarm onto the white sheet. Taking a good hold of the end of the branch I lifted it and gave it two violent shakes to dislodge the cluster onto the sheet. Bees exploded into the air, but the majority fell onto the white sheet. I placed the branch onto the sheet and retired to see what would happen.

The bees were spread all over the sheet and though I didn't see the queen, they started to walk up the ramp and into the hive. I knew the queen would look for the dark entrance, and once in, the others would follow. It was great to see this army of bees some walking, some running, up the white sheet and into the hive. Within about half an hour most of the bees had disappeared inside.

Many were also clustered on the outside wall of the hive and some were still on the branch. A couple more shakes dislodged them and like the others they walked up the ramp. I gave a bit of smoke to some stragglers and then told the wedding party we should leave them and I would return at dusk.

I returned as it was getting dark to find that no bees were left on the sheet but a few were flying around the hive. I gave the air around the hive a few puffs of smoke, and though a handful of bees would not go in, I sealed the entrance with gaffer tape, pleased with myself for collecting the vast majority.

I now needed to make the hive safe to transport home in my car. I used two ratchet straps to strap the hive so it couldn't come apart. I then lifted it onto a dustsheet, large enough to gather up and tie together at the top. Once this was completed I loaded the hive into the car.

Once home I unwrapped the sheet, removed the straps, placed the hive in my chosen location, and unsealed the entrance. By now it was nearly dark and I quickly managed to get a rapid feeder in place before night fell. Using a 1:1 sugar solution, I left the feeder on for a number of days, until they had drawn out much of the wax foundation. I'm pleased to say this colony did not vacate their new home and are thriving well.

In this instance I had an empty hive. However, chances are you might not have one available. Of course it depends on where you locate a swarm, but getting it into a box will enable you to get it home and give you time to sort out the hiving.

If the position of a swarm allows you to get a skep or even a large cardboard box over it, smoking below it will encourage the bees to climb up into it.

Bees are actually quite docile when they swarm because they will have taken in a few days' supply of feed. I have collected many more swarms since this first one. With one, I used a box over the cluster and smoked them into a nucleus box hanging from a tree: another, I brushed into a container. For this swarm,

I placed a wine box with a ramp leading to the holes I had drilled into it. I covered the ramp with a small white cloth. As I swept the bees into a container, I emptied it over the ramp and the bees happily climbed up and into the box.

Once the swarm is contained within a sealed box wrapped in a securely tied sheet, it's easy to transport it home in your car. If you need time to prepare a hive when you reach home, place the sheeted box on the ground, untie it and make a small entrance by placing a block under one corner of the box. The bees will soon settle and treat this as their new home. The only problem is you can't feed them.

When you are ready to hive them, the preferred method is to shake them out to allow them to climb into the hive via a sheeted ramp. Another quick method is to open the hive, remove the crown board and dump the colony from the box straight over the frames. It's not very dignified, but as long as the queen goes into the hive, the rest of the bees will follow.

A perfectly shaped swarm cluster low down on a garden bush

Hints & tips

- When hiving a swarm, getting the queen to enter the hive, skep or box is the key. Once she is in the others will follow.

- If you want the chance to collect swarms in your area, have swarm equipment ready in advance, so if you get a call you can move at a moment's notice.

99

Your second year

"The Spring clean"

With spring arriving and your bees busy bringing in nectar and pollen, you will need to give your hives a clean. Bees like clean living and will keep their hives relatively clean; a little help from us will help to keep the hive disease free. As it is the start of your second season, the spring clean is not too complicated, but with some forward thinking and planning, you can make certain you have everything with you when you open the hive.

Wait for a warm sunny day, but although the weather will be warmer than it has been, you will need to work quickly so you don't let all the heat escape from the hive. Although this is not an inspection, keep an eye open as you work through the hive. As well as your normal equipment of bee suit, smoker and hive tool, you will need the following items:

1. New or cleaned wire mesh floor and entrance block
2. New or cleaned brood box
3. New or cleaned dummy board
4. New or cleaned crown board

Once you are ready to open the hive, have everything at hand with the clean brood box alongside sitting on blocks off the ground. I also place a mite board on the blocks to catch any bees that might fall.

Remove the roof and crown board from the hive to be cleaned, leaning the crown board against the entrance. Remove the dummy board and place it in the roof. Then remove each frame, placing them in exactly the same position in the clean brood box.

As you lift out each frame, you should notice the first and last few frames have capped food stores. This, and the position of any other food stores, will give you a good indication as to whether your bees need any spring feeding.

As you get closer to the central frames you should see capped brood cells with capped honey above the brood. If this is the case, then the food is ideally positioned close to where the queen is laying her eggs. If there is honey on the outer frames, but a limited amount of capped food close to any brood, I suggest you give the hive a spring feed.

This process of exchanging the frames from the used brood box to a new or cleaned one should only take you a minute or two. Once the frame transfer is complete, remove the old empty brood box and the used wire mesh floor. Put in place the clean mesh floor and entrance block and then place the clean brood box containing the transferred frames on top.

Lever the frames gently into their position and place a clean dummy board as the last frame. Before closing the hive give the old brood box, dummy board and crown board a firm shake over the frames to dislodge any bees still clinging to them.

To close the hive, add a clean crown board, cover the feed holes and finally fit the roof. Your bees now have a nice clean home. There will still be bees clinging onto the old hive parts. Leave them leaning against the entrance, and as the day cools the bees will soon make their way home to join the rest. You can return at dusk to collect these hive parts.

In subsequent years you will do this spring-clean annually. However you may also need to replace old frames of brood comb that has discoloured.

In your third year, you will need to start exchanging new frames of foundation for old comb, but it's not something to worry about at this stage.

Lightly toast corners and cracks with a blowtorch to kill any bugs and diseases

Burr comb built up on the underside of the crown board

Depending on the weather conditions each spring, you may find that things are progressing rapidly at this stage in the hive. Indicators are plenty of capped brood and even a build up of burr comb on the underside of the crown board. If this is the case, your bees might need a bit more room for expansion.

As I mentioned earlier, it's better to place a super too early than too late. If you feel your bees could do with the space, add a queen excluder onto the brood box with a sheet of newspaper over it and place a super with frames on top. If you have some frames from the previous year, from which the wax foundation has been drawn out, help your bees and place three or four frames in the super. Alternate these frames between new foundation and the drawn frames. The newspaper is there to act as insulation, as the super above will be cold. This is just like insulation in your attic at home, which keeps the rooms below warm, but the attic quite cold.

As the days warm, and your bees want to expand upwards, they will soon chew holes through the paper to allow them access into the super. When you do your first full inspection of the year, and see that the bees are using the super, you can remove what remains of the newspaper.

Above: Annually spring cleaning all the hives

Opposite: A beekeeping couple inspecting their hives

Having removed the used brood box, floor and crown board, you can clean them to reuse or to start another hive. You will see that your bees have deposited propolis in all the corners and edges. It's sticky and messy, but use your hive tool to remove it and any burr comb.

Using a blowtorch, lightly toast the inside corners and gaps to kill potential bugs and diseases which might be harbouring there. Don't set the wood on fire: you only need to burn these areas to a light toffee colour.

With the torching done, I give the outside of the wood a quick rub over with some fine sandpaper. This removes any dirt and mould that has collected on the hive whilst it has been subjected to the elements. You can then treat the timber with a wood preservative making the hive parts look new again.

Hives are not cheap, so a little extra work now will see they last many years. That said it's worth remembering that red cedar will last for years without being treated with preservatives.

Third season

Generally, throughout your third and subsequent seasons, you'll follow the same procedures you've practiced from the start. However, it is in your third season and beyond that you will need to start exchanging old brood frames.

As time passes you'll notice that the brood comb will age becoming dark brown in colour. This is due to your bees' constant movement over the comb and their feet, dirty from foraging outside, discolouring it. Over time the cells will become smaller in size from the bees entering and polishing them inside. Long term, as the cells

reduce in size, it will cause newly emerging bees to be smaller.

Exchanging old frames for new ones is good hive management. When pollen and nectar are in full flow, the outside frames can be removed and replaced with new frames of foundation. As the bees draw these out, further frames can be removed moving the new drawn frames gradually into the central part of the hive.

Over two seasons you should have been able to replace all the frames for new ones. If you are unfortunate enough to find one of your hives has recently swarmed (it happens to us all) you will find many empty frames where all the brood has emerged, leaving the cells empty of eggs and larvae.

The new virgin queen has not yet started to lay her eggs in these cells, so take this opportunity exchange some old frames with new frames of foundation. You can't do them all, as the bees will need some food on the frames and the new queen will need cells to start laying in. It's a good start though if you can replace a few of the frames.

Hints & tips

- Burr comb being built on the underside of the crown board is a good indication that your bees need more space.

As can be seen in the top photograph the older comb has darkened.
Where as newly drawn comb is a light buttery colour

Swarm prevention

"In your second season Splitting a hive"

As spring turns to summer, and your bees are rapidly collecting nectar and pollen, during your weekly inspections you will see that the brood box is filling with frames full of larvae and capped brood.

Creating an artificial swarm

Although you have added a super or two to give your bees more space, as bees emerge, the brood box will become very congested and the bees' natural instinct is to divide the colony. Swarming can occur with half the colony leaving the hive to look for a new home. Losing half the colony will not help us to maximise our honey harvest, so we need to take steps to prevent the hive swarming.

The bees will produce queen cells to produce a new queen as the colony increases in size. Once the cell is capped, the old queen will depart taking half the colony with her. The new virgin queen will soon mate once she emerges and the remaining bees will continue foraging and feeding the new eggs she has laid. But of course, until the brood emerges and the colony develops again, the numbers in the colony are half what they were.

Bees generally swarm through May, June and July, so near the end of April and through this period, you need to keep a very close look out for queen cells when you make your inspections.

You can pinch or cut queen cells out when you see them forming but you won't prevent the bees continuing to produce queen cells. Bees are very adept at hiding these cells away so the more you remove them, the harder they will become to spot.

If you allow the bees to build queen cells, and don't remove them, they are reasonably easy to spot. About an inch in size and resembling a large acorn, they are usually found hanging in the middle of a frame of brood or on the bottom edge of a frame. They can be a single cell or in a row of two or three.

You will need to act to prevent your hive from swarming if you do spot them. It takes 16 days from the egg being laid to the virgin queen hatching. However, the colony will swarm soon after the cell is capped, which is approximately eight days from when the egg was laid. So inspecting your hives weekly should enable you to spot and prevent swarming within this period.

A queen cell hanging from the middle of a frame

A polystyrene nucleus box alongside a wooden travel box

Both do the same job in transferring bees. The polystyrene nucleus box has an internal feeder for sugar solution and can be used to over-winter a small colony on six frames.

We need to split the hive to trick the bees into thinking they have swarmed themselves. Doing this isn't difficult. A bit of pre-planning helps when creating an artificial swarm, so make sure you have everything you need to split the hive.

Equipment you will need:

1. Clean wire mesh floor and stand

2. Clean entrance block

3. Clean brood box with frames of foundation

4. Two clean queen excluders

First, place the equipment alongside the hive you are going to split.

Place the clean wire mesh floor and stand alongside the hive in the position you want to place the new hive. Open the hive as you would for any inspection and go through each frame in the brood box.

You need to find the queen plus the location of any queen cells. Remove one new frame of foundation from the centre of the new clean brood box and lay this to one side.

A marked queen bee laying an egg in a cell

When you locate the queen, carefully remove the frame she's on with the capped brood and bees and put it in the space you've made in the new brood box.

Remove the old brood box with the queen cells and place it to one side, either on the upturned roof or on blocks. It is to go onto the new clean wire mesh floor and stand.

Place a queen excluder on the old wire mesh floor. Put the new clean brood box with the queen, and frames with new foundation on top of it, then add another queen excluder above the brood box.

The queen will now be in her original hive position. The excluders are in place, top and bottom, to prevent her from eloping should she wish to. You can now add any supers you had in place back on top before adding the crown board and roof. Your original queen is now safely in the hive, still in her original location.

Next, place the old brood box on top of the new mesh floor in the new hive position. Slowly go through each frame, shaking off the bees except from the frame with the queen cell you want to keep.

Hints & tips

- Place brood boxes or supers on the upturned roof or blocks so they don't come into contact with the ground.

When choosing the queen cell you want to hatch, choose one with a larva inside rather than one that's nearly capped so you know that there is something inside.

Remember which frame has your chosen queen cell, then check you haven't missed any others. Shaking off the bees will help you to see the frames and brood more clearly. It's vital you don't shake the queen cell you want to keep as this could damage or dislodge the larva.

If you do find other queen cells, or you suspect you can see cells being constructed, pinch or cut them out.

Once you're happy there is only one queen cell, replace a frame of new foundation in the gap from which you removed the queen. Then you can close up this hive.

You have now successfully split the hive.

To recap, you now have two hives. One hive with the queen in her original position, and a new, second hive with a queen cell from which a virgin queen will emerge in a few days.

As the day progresses the bees that were foraging will return to find their queen. Any other foraging bees that are now in the second hive will depart and return to the position of their original hive. The new hive will be left with young nurse bees and most of the brood from the original hive. These young nurse bees have never flown or left the hive so they don't know that their location has been changed.

The original hive will think they have swarmed naturally as the size of the colony is now dramatically reduced. The queen on only one frame of brood will want to continue laying eggs. So, the bees within the hive will rapidly draw out

the wax foundation in the other frames to produce comb for her to lay eggs in.

Although there won't be any food in the brood box, the supers on top will have enough food in them to see the bees through until the foundation is drawn out, the queen is laying, and they have placed food stocks close by. Leave the hive for a couple of weeks and then continue with your weekly inspections. Remember to remove the second queen excluder, which is below the brood box, during your next inspection.

Within the new hive, the nurse bees will continue feeding any uncapped larvae, and as they mature, will soon be out foraging themselves. The capped brood will continue emerging to become the new nurse bees.

Within three days of emerging, your virgin queen will have flown and mated, and returned to the hive to start her cycle of egg laying.

Leave the hive for a couple weeks after the queen has emerged and then do a quick inspection to see if she has started laying eggs. It may take three weeks before you see any. Though the colony will increase with the emerging brood, and space might become tight again, it's unlikely they will swarm.

After this two to three week period, and once you see new brood, you can add supers to aid them with space. Although it's unlikely they will swarm a second time, it's not unknown for a hive to produce a cast swarm. You can prevent this by cutting out any queen cells you see appearing after you've split the hive.

Ideally you will place your new hive exactly where you need it. However, on one occasion, I found I wanted the new hive to be about 100 metres away in another location.

A newly formed queen cup within a frame

I left the hive alone for a couple of days to allow any foraging bees to find their way back to the queen in the original hive. Then, late one evening, I sealed the entrance of the new hive and strapped the hive and stand together with ratchet straps.

With the help of a friend, I slowly and carefully moved it the 100 metres to its new location, taking care not to damage the queen cell. Once it was in its new location I opened the entrance. It was then in place to continue its production.

Remember though, if you can't move the hive within this two-day period, the bees are maturing and will soon be out foraging. Also the new queen may not have hatched and mated.

If this is the case, you will need to leave the hive in place for three weeks to allow her time to mate. You don't want her to return to the hive after mating only to find it isn't there. Be patient. If you still want to relocate the hive, move it first to a site over three miles away for two weeks before bringing it back to your new location.

Hints & tips

- The golden rule is you can move a hive up to three feet or over three miles – nothing in between.

Creating a nucleus

Even if you decide you don't want more hives you will still need to take steps to prevent your hive from swarming. Another way to do this is to create a nucleus that you can give or sell on to another beekeeper. Your local association will have a growing list of new beekeepers desperate to get hold of their first colony of bees.

Creating a five or six frame nucleus is simple but you will need to have a nucleus box to make the transfer. Whoever takes delivery of the nucleus should return the box to you, with new frames of foundation, once they have transferred the bees on frames into their hive.

To create the nucleus, place the empty nucleus box alongside the hive you are going to split.

Open the hive and go through each frame slowly to search for the queen and any queen cells. You only want one queen cell to remain in the hive, so pinch or cut out any others. The frame with the queen cell needs to remain in the hive, so remember where it is.

You will need to give the nucleus some food stores, so select a couple of frames of brood which also have some capped stores and place them in the nucleus as the two outside frames.

Transfer the frame of brood with the queen onto the centre of the nucleus and then add two or three further frames of brood and bees. When you have made the transfer, place the lid on the nucleus box.

You will need to replace the frames you removed from your original hive with new frames of wax foundation. Once these are in place, you can close the hive with the queen excluder and supers in place as they were before.

The nucleus box has mesh holes for ventilation but make sure you open the entrance hole. The box can now remain in place until it is collected: ideally on the same day.

It's best if the new beekeeper waits until evening to collect the nucleus, to allow any foraging bees to return. At dusk, once all the bees have returned, seal the entrance and screw or strap down the lid. The nucleus can now be safely transported in the back of a car. The new owner should place the nucleus in their chosen location, open the entrance and transfer the frames into their own hive within 24 hours.

Opposite: A nucleus of bees with a feeder in place, ready for collection by a new beekeeper

Many experienced beekeepers have different ways in which they split or create a nucleus hive. Your instructor and members of your local association will suggest a variety of methods. Listen to them as there is more than one way to do it. Experiment, practise and see which method suits you.

To maximise hive production, some beekeepers do not wait for a queen cell to hatch. They minimise the risk of the virgin queen getting lost, not mating or being eaten by a bird for example, before she returns to the hive.

If you are concerned this might happen, you will need to remove all queen cells when you split the hive and replace them with a new queen from another source.

Before you introduce a queen, make sure of her origin and that she comes from a reliable source. Queens are introduced into a hive via a cage. This allows her and the colony time to get used to each other before being fully integrated within the hive. The great advantage of introducing a queen, other than replacing a lost queen, is time scale. An introduced queen will very soon be at full production laying eggs. A newly emerged virgin queen will need to mature, mate and return to the hive before being at full productivity.

Final inspection of a nucleus before delivering it to a new beekeeper

Extracting honey

"The Sticky but sumptuous bit"

Your reward for the effort you've put into looking after your bees is all the delicious honey you are going to harvest. No doubt having told friends and family about your hobby, they will be queuing up waiting for their first jar of honey.

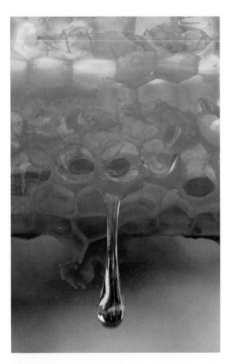

Above: Honey dripping from uncapped comb.

Opposite: Brushing bees from a frame of honey comb "Brush and Run".

Removing supers

Before you can harvest the honey in the supers, you have to check that the bees have reduced the water content. You will know this when you see the frames in the supers capped with a white wax during your inspections.

As with all aspects of beekeeping: think ahead and make a plan. Before you remove the filled supers, prepare all the equipment you need and decide on a room in which to do the extraction. As a hobby beekeeper, this will most likely be your kitchen. Extracting honey can be a messy business. However it's not difficult to clean up afterwards using hot water and a sponge.

Before removing the supers from the hive, you need to remove the bees from within them. If your bees have been collecting pollen and nectar from a variety of sources, you can do this simply by using an ingenuous device called

a Porter Bee Escape. However, if your bees have been on rapeseed, you will have to use the method known as 'brush and run'.

You'll need to fit Porter Bee Escapes to your hives 24 hours in advance of the day on which you decide to do your honey extraction.

To do this, remove the queen excluder placing a crown board between the brood box and supers with the bee escapes in place. Use the crown board in place on the hive if you don't have a spare one, and for this short period, cover the top super with a cloth before fitting the roof.

Porter Bee Escapes are one-way valves. There are holes on top of your crown board that you will have kept covered unless feeding your bees. The Porter Bee Escapes fit into these holes.

Once in place any bees working within the super will descend into the hive to collect further stores or to go out foraging. A spring clip enables them to exit through the bee escape but stops them returning.

You should find the supers empty of bees when you return to remove them after 24-48 hours. Any lingering bees can be easily brushed off. Cover the supers with a cloth and you should be able to get them inside without too many bees following you.

You won't be able to use Porter Bee Escapes if your bees have been (or could have been) on rapeseed. The honey will cool once bees have left the super, unfortunately rapeseed crystallises the honey which makes it impossible to extract. Therefore rapeseed honey has to be extracted immediately the supers have been removed from the hive. You don't want bees on the frames when you're extracting, so you'll need to use the 'brush and run' method.

I got stung a few times on my hands and wrists the first time I carried out the brush and run technique. I now know I was too aggressive with my brushing which bees don't like. I did some research before the following season and found a video clip on the internet. It demonstrated a simple technique that has worked perfectly for me. I've found it very easy to get the bees off the frames and the bee-less supers back into my kitchen by using this method.

You'll need an empty super to attempt this method. It will also help if there are two of you though it's not necessary.

Above: Frame ready for extraction. Honey capped across the frame

With the empty super placed on a cloth or board alongside, remove a frame of honey from the super. Shake it over the hive, which should dislodge most of the bees. However, if this does not work for you, hold one end of the top bar and firmly tap the other end once or twice onto a hard object in front of the hive. (The paving slab the hive is placed on is perfect or have a brick with you).

Hints & tips

- Remove and extract any rapeseed honey as soon as the crop stops flowering in your location.

The bees will fall off leaving only one or two on the frame. Pass the frame to your partner who can brush off the remaining bees before placing the frame into the empty super.

After you've transferred each frame, cover the super immediately with a cloth or spare crown board.

Carry out this procedure for each frame until you have removed them all. When you have transferred all the frames you will have a pile of bees in front of the hive. Don't be concerned as they will be unharmed and will find their way back into the hive. Any other bees close by will be attracted by the honey, so keep the removed frames covered as you work through your hives and take them indoors for immediate extraction.

Above: Porter Bee Escape in place on crown board

Opposite: Uncapping a frame of honey using a capping fork

Dealing with crystallised honey

Honey containing rapeseed nectar will crystallise rapidly. I've found that the extracted honey becomes very thick and it won't pass through either coarse or fine filters. So, the honey needs to be warmed to bring it back to a liquid state.

You can buy a warming cabinet or make one easily. It is an insulated box, large enough to take a honey tank or honey buckets, and has a low heat source. I had an old chest freezer which was an ideal insulated box and a perfect size to take two honey tanks. The only heat source I needed to liquefy the honey was a lit 60-watt light bulb hanging in the freezer with the lid closed.

The honey has to be in place for about 24-48 hours, after which time it will be runny enough to filter. Don't try to speed up the process by using a 100-watt bulb and don't attempt to soften the honey by placing it onto a direct heat such as a gas or electric stove.

Hints & tips

- A super full of honey is heavy (25lbs/11kg) so have a wheelbarrow with you if you have to carry them any distance.

Extracting the honey

With your full supers indoors, ideally in a bee-proof room, the first job before spinning the frames in an extractor is to remove the wax capping. Bee equipment suppliers offer all manner of tools with which to do this. However, the two most used methods for the hobby beekeeper are either a sharp flexible knife or an uncapping fork.

Heated cutting tools are available, but costs probably prohibit their use for beekeepers with just a few hives. Either a knife or fork work well. Dip them into a bowl of hot water between each cut or scrape. Wipe the blade or teeth before you cut as you don't want to add excess water to the honey.

If you are only doing a few frames, place the frame of honey onto a flat tray. I used to use a clean paint roller tray as it holds the frame

allowing you to remove the wax cappings on both sides and catches any honey which drips from the cells. However, if you have a number of hives, a purpose built uncapping tray and frame holder makes life much easier.

You only have to remove the wax capping so do this gently but firmly without going too deep and removing too much comb and honey.

Have an empty bowl alongside you into which you can scrape all the wax cappings or let them drop into the uncapping tray. These cappings can be filtered to collect the honey residue.

You can melt down the remaining wax to make candles, wax polish or even sell it in exchange for new sheets of foundation.

As you go through your frames, you may find sides or parts of a frame with honey which has not been capped. Give it a firm shake to test that the water content of the honey has been reduced. If no honey drips out then you can extract it. If honey does drip out then return that frame for the bees to complete and cap.

Whether you have bought, borrowed or hired an extractor make sure it's very clean and dry before you place the frames inside it to spin.

The smaller tabletop extractors are usually tangential. That means, when spun, each frame has to be removed and turned before you extract the other side.

Place the frames in the extractor following the manufacturer's instructions. A frame of honey is heavy, so with the lid in place, start spinning slowly. Each turn will become lighter as the honey spins out so you can increase the speed.

Above: Spinning frames in a tangential extractor in the kitchen
Notice uncapping tray and frames in place ready for uncapping.

Filtering honey through
a coarse and fine filter

After spinning for a minute, remove the frames and turn them round to extract the other side.

Don't try to spin out all the honey on the first side. It can crush through the comb if you try to empty one side whilst the other is still full. It takes more work, but extracting a little from each side keeps the frames balanced when spinning.

The empty frames of comb can then be returned to the super you removed them from. Continue through each of the frames you need to extract, keeping an eye on the level of honey in the bottom of the extractor. Once the level is high enough, you can open the extractor's honey gate and pour the honey through filters into a honey bucket.

You have a choice of how many and how fine a filter you pour your honey through. Most beekeepers pass the honey through a coarse and a fine filter, which should remove any debris in the honey.

The more times you pour the honey, the more air will get into it. So, when you've completed the extraction, it's essential that the honey sits for a minimum of 24 hours to allow the air bubbles to rise to the surface. Naturally you will be impatient to proudly show off your first jars of honey. But wait and give plenty time for the air to rise because it will improve the quality.

When you have completed the extraction, you can return the empty frames of comb to the hives and the bees will clean them. Wait until the evening to return them so the bees don't get over excited.

If you have extracted honey early in the season the bees will clean the comb and continue to fill them with honey for you to harvest later in the season.

However, when you do your last extraction of the season, allow the bees to clean the comb for two or three days by placing the supers on the hive with a crown board below them.

Open one of the crown board holes a fraction to allow the bees access. The small opening will make the bees think it is not their own honey store and they will clean the comb, taking any residue honey down into the brood box.

After a couple of days put Porter Bee Escapes in place to clear the bees from the supers. The cleaned supers can then be stacked outside well away from the hives. Any lingering bees will return back to their hive as evening falls. Once the cleaned supers and frames are clear of bees you can clean and store them away for winter.

Hints & tips

- After extracting, your honey must sit for 24 hours minimum before you pour it into jars.

Honey

"Jars, Chunk or Comb"

When you've let your honey settle you can pour it into jars. You can buy jars of all shapes and sizes or use clean jars you've collected.

Most honey is sold in 1lb/454gm jars. If you are going to sell it you will need to clearly mark the jar with details of weight, who and where the honey came from, plus the country of origin.

Each country has its own food labelling rules. These rules should be available on the Trading Standards' website or from your local government office that deals with food quality and hygiene.

Pour the honey through the honey gate on your honey tank into the jars and screw the cap on immediately. You'll find you can do this quickly with practise. You'll also be able to judge when each jar is at the correct weight by the level of the honey, or you can weigh it on digital kitchen scales.

Once all the honey is in jars you can apply the labels before storing them at room temperature in a dark place.

Labels are available from many leading equipment suppliers. I want my honey to stand out so I design my own labels and have a new design each year. Many printers can now digitally print label stickers so limited numbers aren't too expensive.

Left: Pouring honey into jars from a honey tank
Opposite: Liquid, comb and chunk honey

You may like to do some jars of chunk honey. If you do, keep a couple of frames back from extraction.

Cut out chunks of honeycomb and place in the jars then top up with liquid honey.
To prevent liquid honey from granulating around the chunks of comb, heat the honey and then let it cool before you place it in the jar with the comb.

See box page 118: Dealing with crystallised honey.

If you like comb honey on its own, you can buy unwired foundation which can't be used in an extractor.

You can buy plastic or wooden containers for comb honey and this is an attractive way to sell or give your honey as a present.

Many hotels would love to offer a full frame of your honey to their guests at breakfast if you have enough to supply them. Honey sitting in a frame stand on a breakfast table makes an impressive sight.

There are a few regulations to bear in mind if you intend to sell your honey. If you are selling small quantities they aren't prohibitive, but it's best to check your local regulations as basic food hygiene handling standards need to be observed.

Locally produced honey is in high demand, so you should be able to find a ready market for it. I have plenty passing traffic and a sign on the road offering honey for sale. This sign attracts many people to stop, so it doesn't take me long to sell my stock.

Local markets and farmers' markets are excellent places to sell your honey and the cost of a stall isn't expensive. Your local shops may be interested in selling some of your honey, but they will want a cut of the sale price.

As a hobby beekeeper you won't produce enough honey to fill a supermarket, so you'll probably sell some and give the rest to friends and family.

Remember to keep a few jars to enjoy. I keep hold of a couple of jars from each extraction annually. I date the jars and it's very interesting to see the changes in colour year on year. It's like collecting vintage wines, without the high values of a Premier Cru.

The Beekeeper's Year

"Month by Month Notes"

Things to remember to do

October

- Prepare hives for winter: ventilation, mouse guards, woodpecker prevention etc.
- Clean and repair equipment

November

- Complete winter feeding
- Heft hives regularly to check weight
- Ensure bees have access to water

December

- Heft hives regularly to check weight
- Check hives for wind, rain damage etc
- Ensure bees have access to water
- Order new equipment for following year
- Possibly treat varroa with oxalic acid (only in broodless colonies)

January

- Heft hives regularly to check weight
- Feed fondant as necessary
- Possibly treat varroa with oxalic acid (only in broodless colonies)

February

- Heft hives regularly to check weight
- Feed fondant as necessary
- Ensure bees have access to water
- Feed sugar syrup to weak colonies
- Add Fumidol B if nosema suspected (after microscope test)
- Construct new hives and prepare equipment

March

- Feed sugar syrup to weak colonies
- Add Fumidol B if nosema suspected (after microscope test)
- Ensure bees have access to water
- Construct new hives and prepare equipment

April

- Feed sugar syrup to weak colonies
- Spring clean: change floors, brood box and crown board
- Get a second opinion if you suspect any diseases
- Add first supers to hive
- Monitor for varroa

May

- Feed sugar syrup if foraging conditions are poor
- Check hives weekly for queen cells.
- Split hives and make up artificial swarms
- Extract rapeseed honey

June

- Feed sugar syrup if foraging conditions are poor
- Mark queens
- Check hives weekly for queen cells.
- Split hives and make up artificial swarms
- Add supers well in advance to prevent congestion

July

- Feed sugar syrup if foraging conditions are poor
- Check hives weekly for queen cells
- Check for space, disease, stores, queen and swarming
- Add supers
- Extract blossom honey

August

- Feed sugar syrup if foraging conditions are poor
- Check hives every 7-9 days for space, disease etc.
- Add supers
- Extract blossom honey
- Cull and replace old queens
- Prevent robbing bees and wasps
- Treat for varroa once supers are removed
- Feed sugar syrup after varroa treatment

September

- Treat for varroa once supers are removed
- Feed sugar syrup after varroa treatment
- Prevent robbing bees and wasps
- Cull and replace old queens
- Complete winter feeding by end of the month

Glossary of terms used in beekeeping

A

Abscond
The action of bees leaving the hive suddenly, leaving it empty.

Alighting board
Slope in front of entrance for bees to land on before entering hive.

American foul brood or AFB
A bacterium disease affecting bee brood. It is highly contagious and has a long life span.

Anaphylactic shock
A strong and possibly fatal reaction to bee stings.

Apiarist
A beekeeper.

Apiary
The area or location where bees and hives are kept.

Apiculture
The science and study of keeping bees.

Apiphobia
The acute fear of or anything related to bees.

Apis mellifera
The scientific name of the Western honey bee.

Apiguard
A miticide used to control varroa mites.

Apitherapy
A division of therapy that uses bees and bee products for therapeutic and medical purposes.

Artificial swarm
Splitting a hive to trick the bees into thinking they have swarmed themselves.

B

Bee bread
Pollen that was collected by bees and then mixed with various solutions, including honey, which is stored within a cell of the comb. This is a high protein feed for both the developing larva and bees.

Bee brush
A long handled, soft haired brush used to gently move bees.

Bee glue
Propolis is an essential anti-bacterial and anti-fungal material collected from plants by bees.

Beehive
A container used by a beekeeper for the purpose of keeping a colony of bees.

Beeswax
A substance that is secreted by the worker bee's glands. This is the primary building material used by bees to build comb.

Brace comb
The sections of seemingly random comb that connect hive parts together. Brace comb is a form of burr comb.

Burr comb
Any section of comb that is not part of the main comb piece within the frame or hanging from the top bar.

Brood
A general term to refer to immature bees. It includes egg, larva and pupae.

Brood box, deep box or chamber
Section of the hive where brood is being raised and where the queen lays her eggs.

Brood food
A highly nutritious glandular secretion from the worker bee that is used to feed both brood and the queen.

C

Canola (rapeseed oil)
An agricultural crop grown for its seed oil and as an animal feed. Its yellow blossom is distinctive in spring-time.

Capped brood
Cells on the comb containing bee larvae that is fully enclosed by a wax capping.

Capping
A thin layer of wax that covers cells containing honey or brood.

Cast swarm
A further swarm from a hive after a colony has swarmed the first time.

Caste
A name for the existence of different classifications of bees of a specific family. Includes queen, drone and worker.

Chalk brood
A fungal infection of the brood. The cells look like they are filled with chalk.

Chunk honey
A jar of honey with a chunk of comb honey in it.

Cell
A single hexagonal chamber that makes up comb. Cells are used to store honey, pollen, nectar and developing brood.

Cleansing flight
The flight made by a bee to cleanse its rectum after a long period of confinement, usually during winter.

Cluster
A mass of bees, often refers to a swarm or when huddled together for winter.

Colony
A collection or family of bees living within a single social unit.

Colony collapse disorder
A major plague affecting whole colonies of bees, at present only in the USA.

Contact feeder
A bucket with mesh opening used to feed bees.

Comb
A double-sided configuration of hexagonal cells made of beeswax. Used by the bees to store food and raise brood.

Comb honey
A chunk of honey cut from the comb.

Commercial
A type of hive or a professional beekeeper.

Crown board
Ceiling of the hive.

D

Dadant
A type of hive.

Dartington
A type of hive.

Deep box
Section of the hive where brood is being raised and where the queen lays her eggs.

Drawn comb
Combs which contain completed cells drawn out of the wax foundation.

Drone
A male bee.

Dummy board
A solid wood frame to fill a space and to prevent the building of brace comb.

E

Eke
A shallow frame of wood the same size as a hive, used to enable spacing for treatments or feeding.

Entrance block
Wooden entrance to a hive, which can be adjusted.

European foul brood
Bacteria which affects the bee brood before it is capped, essentially by competing for food.

Extraction
Removal of honey from the comb.

Extractor
A centrifugal machine in which honey is spun from the frames.

Feeders
Appliances used to feed bees artificially.

Fondant
Solid sugar feed used as a feed supplement.

Foragers
The bees that leave the hive to collect pollen and nectar.

Foul brood
Generic term to describe a bacterial disease that affects brood.

Foundation
A thin sheet of wax that is embossed to be used as a guide for comb creation by the bees. Can be wired or not.

Frame
A rectangular segment made of four slats of wood that is made to contain comb.

Fumadil B
An antibiotic used to control nosema, which is sold under the trade name of *Fumadil B*.

Fumagillin
An antibiotic used to control nosema, which is sold under the trade name of *Fumadil B*.

Guard bee
A bee that remains at the entrance of a hive protecting it from invaders.

Guarding
The action of a bee that detects invaders and examines entering bees.

Heft/hefting
Lifting a corner of a hive to feel the weight and how much food is in the hive.

Hive
Home for an individual colony of managed bees.

Hive tool
A bladed and hooked bar used by beekeepers to maintain and manage a hive.

Hoffman self-spacing frame
Frames with end bars wider at the top than the bottom providing bee space between frames when they are placed in a hive.

Honey bucket
Container used to collect and settle honey after extraction.

Honeycomb
Comb that has been nearly or completely filled with honey.

Honey flow
A period of time when an abundance of nectar is available to be collected and converted into honey.

Langstroth
A type of hive.

Larva/Larvae
The second stage of development in bee's life cycle.

Laying worker
An unfertilised, non-queen female bee capable of laying drone eggs. This is often the result of a hive remaining queenless for a period of time.

Landing board
Projection just below hive entrance, often sloping.

Mandibles
The bees' jaws, used for cutting, gripping and to hold enemies in a fight.

Marked queen
A queen bee that has been marked with a spot of paint.

Mesh floor
Wire mesh floor below brood box to allow debris and dead mites to fall through.

Miticide
A chemical or biological agent that is applied to a colony to control parasitic mites.

Mouse guard
Metal guard attached to hive entrance to prevent mice entering.

National
A type of hive.

Nectar
A food source, high in carbohydrates, which occurs naturally in the nectarines of a flower.

Nectar flow
The mass gathering of nectar from flowers by bees.

Nest
An unmanaged wild colony of bees, often found in the hollow of a tree, wall partition, attic, etc.

Nosema
An illness that affects the digestive tract in bees.

Nuc or nucleus box/ hive
A small colony of bees housed within a smaller hive container with five or six frames.

Nuptial flight
The mating flight taken by a queen to mate with a variety of drones.

Nurse bee
Young hive-bound bee that feeds and cares for the larvae.

Pheromone
A chemical scent excreted by bees to establish a form of communication or to stimulate a response to danger.

Pollen
The powdery substance produced by the male segment of a flower.

Porter Bee Escape
A device fitted to a crown board just before extraction of honey. A one-way valve enables bees to be cleared from a super.

Propolis
Propolis is an essential anti-bacterial and anti-fungal material collected from plants by bees. Also used to strengthen hive, comb and to fill cracks within the hive.

Pupa
The final stage in a bee's metamorphosis.

Queen
The fertile female bee that once mated should be capable of producing male and female offspring.

Queen cage
A device used to trap the queen to enable her to be marked or to be held for other reasons.

Queen clipping
Removing a portion of one or both front wings of a queen to prevent her from flying.

Queen cup
A cup-shaped cell hanging vertically from the comb, but containing no egg.

Queen excluder
A device used to prevent the larger queen bee and drones from passing through.

Rapeseed oil (Canola)
An agricultural crop grown for its seed oil and as an animal feed. Its yellow blossom is distinctive in springtime.

Rapid feeder
A container placed on a hive to feed bees.

Robbing bee
Foreign bee attempting to steal honey from a hive.

133

Royal Jelly
A substance produced by worker bees to feed to the youngest brood and to the queen throughout its life.

Scout bee
A bee that is responsible for finding daily nectar and pollen sources as well as finding a new home for a swarm of bees.

Sealed
Honey or brood that has been capped with a thin layer of wax.

Skep
A wicker basket used to collect swarms. Originally used as hives.

Smith
A type of hive.

Smoker
A tool used to blow cool smoke over the hive.

Solar wax extractor
Glass-covered insulated box used to melt wax from combs and cappings using the heat of the sun.

Splitting a hive
Method used to create an artificial swarm, tricking the bees into thinking they have swarmed themselves.

Sting
Bee's defence mechanism, capable of releasing venom into its victim.

Sugar solution
A mixture of dissolved sugar and water fed to bees.

Supersede - supersedure
The natural process of a bee colony replacing its queen with a new one without the colony swarming.

Super
A box placed on a hive with frames to collect honey.

Supering
The act and process of adding hive boxes to a hive to collect honey for harvesting.

Swarm
A collection of bees that is currently without a home site and is looking for a new one.

Terramycin
An antibiotic used for the treatment of bacterial disease.

Top bar
The top part of a frame.

Top bar hive
A type of hive originally found in Africa, but also in Ancient Greece.

Uncapping knife or fork
Tools used to shave off the cappings of sealed honey before extraction.

Uncapping tank
Container over which frames of honey are uncapped, used to collect any residue honey.

Varroa
A parasitic mite that attaches itself to bees.

Veil
A protective netting to cover a beekeeper's face.

Virgin queen
An unmated queen bee.

Waggle dance
A figure of eight motion carried out by bees to indicate location of a pollen/nectar source.

Wax moth
Galleria mellonella and achroia grisella – two types of moth whose larvae bore through and destroy honeycomb.

WBC
A type of hive.

Winter cluster
A tightly packed cluster of bees that forms to maintain warmth during the colder winter months.

Worker
An unfertilised female bee that forms the majority of a colony's population.

Pollen Colour Guide

I thoroughly enjoy watching my bees come and go from the hives. If I stand behind the hives with the sun at the correct angle, I can make out for some distance the direction they are heading in and out.

I often wonder where they are going, because although I see many bees collecting water from my garden pond, I see very few actually working the flowers in the garden.

It's fascinating to see the variety of colours of pollen on their legs when they return. Depending on the season I can guess what pollen they are returning to the hive with.

Rapeseed pollen in May is easy to spot as the bees' bodies are dusted in it. In autumn I can spot the ivy pollen as the ivy is very close to the hives. However, I have no clue to the source of most pollen.

I have researched a number of books and on the internet to put together my simple pollen colour guide. Hopefully it will help you work out what your bees are working on.

The guide is not scientific as it's very difficult to depict exact colours in a book. This is because pollen colours vary depending on location and times of the year, and because of the variations in colour printing.

I hope you have some fun using it and that it gives you an idea of where your bees have been.

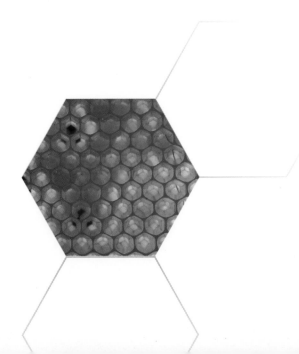

Guide to Pollen Colours

Maple
Early Spring

Snowdrop
Early Spring

Crocus
Early Spring

Hazel
Early Spring

Elm
Early Spring

Gorse
Early Spring

Aconite
Early Spring

Yew
Early Spring

Willow
Early Spring

Blackthorn
Spring

Poplar
Spring

Wild Cherry
Spring

Gooseberry
Spring

Laurel
Spring

Dandelion
Spring

Apple
Spring

Oak
Spring

Pear
Spring

Wild Cherry
Spring

Plum
Spring

Beech / Lilac
Spring

Copper Beech
Spring

Wild Bluebell
Spring

Sycamore
Spring

Red Horse Chestnut
Spring

Horse Chestnut
Spring

Hawthorn
Spring

Oil Seed Rape
Spring

Elder
Spring

Lupin
Spring

Broad Bean
Spring

Raspberry
Spring

Poppy
Summer

Clover
Summer

Honeysuckle
Summer

Sweet Corn
Summer

Sunflower
Summer

Blackberry
Summer

Lavender
Summer

Lime
Summer

Asparagus
Summer

Hemp
Summer

Ragwort
Summer

Aster
Summer

Pumpkin
Summer

Onion
Summer

Privet
Summer

Ivy
Late Summer

The end

"If you've got to this stage, congratulations you're a beekeeper!"

I hope you've enjoyed this book and have found each of the stages in beekeeping easy to follow.

There are so many more aspects to beekeeping, which perhaps I could have added. For example in future years you may want to rear queens or press heather honey, but I have no experience of these skills.

There are many different facets of beekeeping, but I believe in trying to keep things simple. Even when we have a few decades of beekeeping under our belts, you and I will still be learning. The purpose of this book is simply to pass on the basics of beekeeping as I have learnt them.

I hope you, as I do, will thoroughly enjoy just sitting and watching your bees from time to time. They are fascinating creatures.

At times I have been completely baffled by what my bees are doing. I've watched them come and go, laden down with pollen. I've seen them fight off wasps and at times seen them crash land onto the landing board, thinking to myself, "who gave her a flying licence?"

Other times I have wanted to tear my hair out, though I have learnt it's best to leave them alone when you feel like that. Bees are wild creatures and have been on this planet far longer than us. They have evolved quite successfully without our meddling.

It's June once again as I complete this revised edition. I now have eight colonies in hives, which are strong and rapidly filling the supers with honey. I promised my wife seven hives was enough, but I caught another swarm and had an empty hive... well that's my excuse!

I've made my first extraction of the year, post rapeseed, and with the better than normal English summer, I expect to do a second extraction shortly with a final one in early August.

Hopefully you will soon have your first colony and this book will help you to look after your bees. I hope you will get the same pleasure from them as I do.

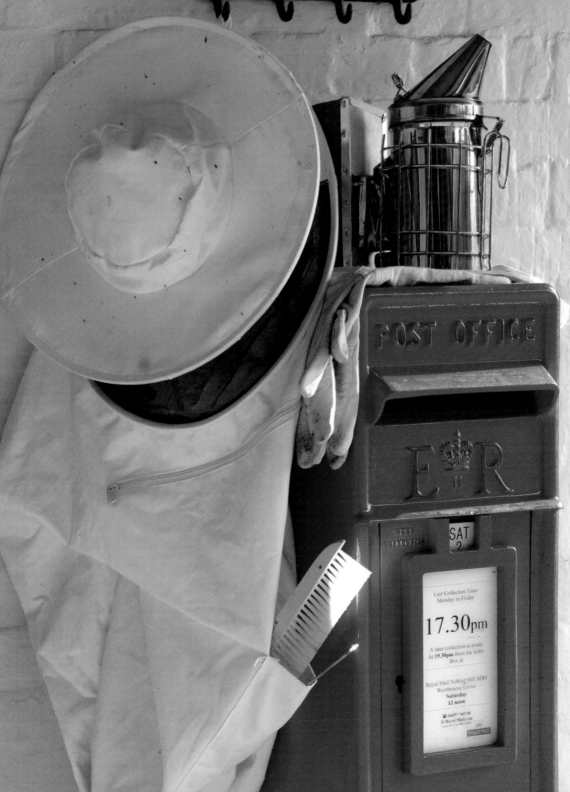

Website links

National Associations and Government Agricultural websites

United Kingdom

British Beekeeping Association (BBKA)
www.bbka.org.uk

Department for Environment Food and Rural Affairs (DEFRA)
www.defra.gov.uk/foodfarm/growing/bees/index.htm

International Bee Research Association (IBRA)
www.ibra.org.uk

Food and Environment Research Agency (FERA)
www.fera.defra.gov.uk

Scotland

www.scottishbeekeepers.org.uk

Wales

www.wbka.com

Northern Ireland

www.ubka.org

Ireland

www.irishbeekeeping.ie

Australia

www.honeybee.com.au

Canada

www.honeycouncil.ca

New Zealand

www.nba.org.nz

United States

www.abfnet.org

USDA Agricultural Research Department
www.ars.usda.gov

South Africa

www.beekeepers.co.za

France

www.unaf.net

Germany

www.deutscherimkerbund.de

Italy

www.cra-api.it

Bee Keeping Suppliers

United Kingdom

E.H. Thorne (Beehives) Ltd
www.thorne.co.uk
Rand: 01673 858555
Windsor: 01753 830256
Newburgh: 01337 842596
Stockbridge: 01264 810916

Paynes Southdown Bee Farms
www.paynesbeefarm.co.uk
Tel: 01273 843388

Cheshire Bee Hives
www.cheshirehives.co.uk
Tel: 0161 669 6241

Bee Basic
www.beebasic.co.uk
Tel: 0208 866 3864

Maisemore Apiaries
www.bees-online.co.uk
Tel: 01452 700289

National Bee Supplies
www.beekeeping.co.uk
Tel: 01837 54085

Easy Bee Products
www.easybeeproducts.co.uk
Tel: 01452 862420

Honey Frame Packaging Company
www.honeyframepackaging.co.uk
Tel: 01747 828075

Honey Labels
www.dw-photography.co.uk
Tel: 01366 324346

Ireland

Shanvaus Apiaries
www.shanvaus-apiary-online.net

Australia

Penders Beekeeping Supplies
www.penders.net.au
Redpaths Beekeeping Supplies
www.redpaths.com.au
Bob's Beekeeping Supplies
www.bobsbeekeeping.com.au
Bindaree Bee Supplies
www.bindaree.com.au

Canada

The Bee Works
www.beeworks.com
Countryfields Bee Keeping
Supplies
www.countryfields.ca
Benson Beekeeping Supplies
www.bensonbee.com
Better Bee Supplies
www.betterbees.com
Munro Honey
www.munrohoney.com
Vancouver Island Apiary Supplies
www.thebeestore.com

New Zealand

Ecroyd Beekeeping Supplies
www.ecroyd.com
Ceracell Beekeeping Supplies
www.bees.co.nz

United States

Betterbee
www.betterbee.com
Mann Lake
www.mannlakeltd.com
Beecare
www.beecare.com
Brushy Mountain Bee Farm
www.brushymountainbeefarm.com
Arnold Honey Bee Services
www.arnoldhoneybeeservices.com

South Africa

Honeybadger
www.honeybadger.co.za
Beeware Beekeeping Supplies
www.beeware.co.z

France

Ickowicz Apiculture
www.ickowicz-apiculture.com
Luberon Apiculture
www.apiculture.net
Lapi
www.lapi.fr

Credit: Photo: Paul Garner

Author and photographer: David Wootton

I am a commercial photographer based on my family's farm in the West Norfolk Fens.
I bought my first camera in 1977 and started out as a keen amateur.

In 1989 whilst living in the French Alpine town of Chamonix, I discovered the relatively new sport of paragliding. I soon discovered there was a market for my photographs of the sport taken from the air in the Mont Blanc region.

I set up as a commercial photographer when I returned to the UK in 1994, offering imagery to businesses to promote and market their company and products. I also specialise in aerial photography, doing annual site surveys for major companies in landfill, construction and quarrying.

I have also covered much of the UK for the RSPB, photographing their bird reserves from the air.

I have travelled extensively around the world on private projects and for magazine clients. Covering such diverse subjects as - orang-utans on Borneo, tigers in India, and the world's largest food fight in La Tomatina in Spain, to name just three.

My work has been published in over 200 magazines and newspapers worldwide plus numerous books. I married Helen in 2008, and I took up beekeeping in the same year.

Please visit my website at
www.dw-photography.co.uk
to view a broad range of my photographic work.

Blog
Please visit
www.beekeeping-book.com/blog/
to follow my beekeeping blog, which is regularly updated with information and photographs.

"There is no other field of animal husbandry like beekeeping. It has the appeal to the scientist, the nature lover and even (or especially) the philosopher. It is a chance to work with some of the most fascinating of God's creatures, to spend time and do work in the great outdoors, to challenge my abilities and continue to learn. My hope is that I never become so frail with old age that I cannot spend my days among the bees. It gives credence to the old saw that "the best things in life are free". I thank God daily for the opporunity and privilege to be a beekeeper".

Author Unknown

Colourful Dadant hives in the Jura mountain region of France.